Key Stage 3
Developing Numeracy

NUMBERS AND THE NUMBER SYSTEM

ACTIVITIES FOR TEACHING NUMERACY

year
8

Hilary Koll and Steve Mills

A & C BLACK

Contents

Published 2003 by A & C Black Publishers Limited
37 Soho Square, London W1D 3QZ
www.acblack.com

ISBN 0-7136-6466-5

Copyright text © Hilary Koll and Steve Mills, 2003
Copyright illustrations © Sue Woollatt, 2003
Copyright cover illustration © Paul Cemmick, 2003
Editors: Lynne Williamson and Marie Lister
Designer: Kim Sillitoe

The authors and publishers would like to thank David Chadwick, Corinne McCrum and Mary Nathan for their advice in producing this series of books.

A CIP catalogue record for this book is available from the British Library.

Printed in Great Britain by St Edmundsbury Press Ltd, Bury St Edmunds, Suffolk.

A & C Black uses paper produced with elemental chlorine-free pulp, harvested from managed sustainable forests.

Introduction

Key Stage 3 **Developing Numeracy: Numbers and the Number System** is a series of photocopiable resources for Years 7, 8 and 9, designed to be used during maths lessons. The books focus on the Numbers and the Number System strand of the Key Stage 3 National Strategy *Framework for teaching mathematics*.

Each book supports the teaching of mathematics by providing a series of activities that develop essential skills in numeracy. The activities aim to reinforce learning and develop the skills and understanding explored during whole-class teaching. Each task provides practice and consolidation of an objective contained in the framework document. On the whole the activities are designed for pupils to work on independently, either individually or in pairs, although occasionally some pupils may need support.

The activities in **Numbers and the Number System Year 8** relate to the following topics:

- place value, ordering and rounding;
- integers, powers and roots;
- fractions, decimals, percentages, ratio and proportion.

How to use this book

Each double-page spread is based around a Year 8 objective. The spread has three main sections labelled A, B and C, and ends with a challenge (**Now try this!**). The work grows increasingly difficult from A through to C, and the 'Now try this!' challenge reinforces and extends pupils' learning. The activities provide the teacher with an opportunity to make informal assessments: for example, checking that pupils are developing mental strategies, have grasped the main teaching points, or whether they have any misunderstandings.

This double-page structure can be used in a variety of ways: for example, following whole-class teaching the pupils can begin to work through both sheets and will experience gradually more complex questions, or the teacher can choose the most appropriate starting points for each group in the class, with some pupils starting at A and others at B or C. This allows differentiation for mixed-ability groups. 'Now try this!' provides a greater challenge for more able pupils. It can involve 'Using and Applying' concepts and skills, and provides an opportunity for classroom discussion. Where appropriate, pupils can be asked to finish tasks for homework.

The instructions are presented clearly to enable pupils to work independently. There are also opportunities for pupils to work in pairs and groups, to encourage discussion and co-operation. A calculator icon indicates whether or not calculators should be used for different parts of the activities. Where there is no icon, the teacher or pupils may choose whether or not to use them. Brief notes are provided at the foot of each page to assist the pupil or classroom assistant, or parent if the sheets are used for homework. Remind the pupils to read these before beginning the activity.

In some cases, the pupils will need to record their workings on a separate piece of paper, and it is suggested that these workings are handed in with the activity sheets. The pupils will also need to record their answers to some of the 'Now try this!' challenges on another piece of paper.

Organisation

Very little equipment is needed, other than the essential rulers, pencils and so on, but for some activity sheets pupils will need algebraic calculators. These activity sheets allow opportunities for pupils to explore keys and interpret the display on the calculator, considering issues such as rounding. It is important in some cases that the calculators used have certain keys, for example a sign change key. During the teaching input, discuss how such keys can be shown in different ways on different calculators, for example $+/-$ or $(-)$.

To help teachers select appropriate learning experiences for pupils, the activities are grouped into sections within the book to match the objectives in the Key Stage 3 National Strategy *Yearly teaching programmes*. However, the activities do not have to be used in the order given. The sheets are intended to support, rather than direct, the teacher's planning.

Some activities can be made easier or more challenging by masking or substituting some of the numbers. You may wish to re-use some pages by copying them onto card and laminating them, or by enlarging them onto A3 paper. They could also be made into OHTs for whole-class use.

Teachers' notes

Extra brief notes, containing specific instructions or points to be raised during the first part of the lesson, are provided for particular sheets (see pages 6–7).

Whole-class oral and mental starters

The following activities provide some practical ideas to support the main teaching part of the lesson, and can be carried out before pupils use the activity sheets.

Place value, ordering and rounding

Multiply and divide

Show the pupils six cards marked ×, ÷, 10, 100, 0.1 and 0.01, and discuss the relative values of the numbers. Then call out any two- or three-digit number, such as 67, and ask a pupil to pick a sign card and a number card to create a question: for example 67 ÷ 0.1. Write this question on the board. Discuss the eight questions that can be created by multiplying or dividing this number by any of those on the cards: 67 × 10, 67 × 100, 67 × 0.1, 67 × 0.01, 67 ÷ 10, 67 ÷ 100, 67 ÷ 0.1, 67 ÷ 0.01. Examine which of the questions have the same answer and group these in pairs, for example 67 × 0.01 and 67 ÷ 100.

Integers, powers and roots

Show me

Give each pupil two sets of 0–9 digit cards. Play 'show me' activities, for example: *Show me a two-digit cube number greater than 50; Show me the square root of 144; Show me a multiple of 17 between 50 and 70; Show me any two-digit prime number between 70 and 80.* Pupils 'show' a number by holding one or two digit cards in the air.

Alphabet sums

Write the letters of the alphabet on the board and give each letter a positive or negative integer value, for example A = 3, B = ⁻10, C = ⁻8, D = 2, and so on. Ask pupils to use this key to find the value of different words or names by adding together the integers, for example CAB = ⁻8 + 3 + ⁻10 = ⁻15. Ask: *Which three-letter words can you find that produce a positive value? Whose name in the class has the greatest value? Is this the person with the most letters in their name?* Pupils could be asked to find words with a particular value: *Can you find a three-letter word with a value of ⁻5?* (BAD).

POSITIVE OR NEGATIVE, SIR?

Fractions, decimals, percentages, ratio and proportion

Percentages

Split the class into up to five teams. Write five percentages across the board in increasing size, for example 5%, 35%, 40%, 75%, 95%. Beneath each percentage write a number decreasing in size, for example 230, 120, 90, 88, 50. Use these as five different percentage questions (5% of 230, 35% of 120, and so on). Ask each team to choose one question that they think has the highest value. They should then find the values of all five percentages. The team (or teams) with the highest value scores a point.

Ratio

Call out a ratio, for example 30 : 50, and ask the pupils to give as many equivalent ratios as possible (6 : 10, 3 : 5, 60 : 100, 15 : 25, and so on). Encourage them to find the most simplified ratio (in this case, 3 : 5), and to use this as a basis to create a pattern of equivalent ratios (3 : 5, 6 : 10, 9 : 15, 12 : 20 and so on). Demonstrate how the numbers in the simplified ratio can be multiplied by any number to create a new equivalent ratio.

Parallel lines

Draw three vertical parallel lines on the board and explain to pupils that they are number lines with 0 at the bottom and 10 at the top. Ask a pupil to put a cross on the first line to show approximately the position of the number 5, on the second line to show the number 1 and finally on the third line to show the number 7. Draw arrows between the three points. Ask pupils by which number you would need to multiply or divide to go from 5 to 1 (÷ 5) and then from 1 to 7 (× 7). Ask how these two operations could be combined to make one multiplication to go from 5 to 7 (× $\frac{7}{5}$). Then ask pupils by which number you could multiply 7 to go back to 5 (× $\frac{5}{7}$). Repeat this activity several times, asking pupils how to go from one number to another, for example from 3 to 8 (× $\frac{8}{3}$) or from 9 to 2 (× $\frac{2}{9}$).

Proportions

On the board, write pairs of numbers with the same proportions, for example 20 → 16, 45 → 36 and 35 → 28. Ask pupils to find other pairs of numbers within the same proportional set and to describe how the numbers are related (in this example, multiplying the first number by $\frac{4}{5}$). Ask pupils to find the second number when given the first, for example 1 → ? ($\frac{4}{5}$) and 6 → ? ($\frac{24}{5}$ or $4\frac{4}{5}$). Discuss how the first number can be found from the second (× $\frac{5}{4}$). Give some examples of second numbers and ask pupils to find the first number, for example ? ← 24 (30) and ? ← 10 ($12\frac{1}{2}$).

Teachers' notes

Place value, ordering and rounding

Pages 8 & 9

During your teaching input, revise column headings for numbers to one billion (one thousand million – nine zeros). Discuss how, when writing large numbers, we group digits in threes from the right-hand side, and how commas are sometimes used to show these groups. Part C involves early ideas of 'standard form', although it is not necessary for pupils to be introduced to this term at this stage.

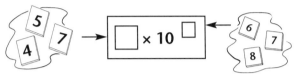

Pages 10 & 11

Begin by revising ways of writing 'one-tenth' and 'one-hundredth', both as fractions and decimals. Discuss their relative sizes and the different contexts in which they are used, for example 'a tenth of a metre', 'a hundredth of a pound'.

Pages 12 & 13

A useful starter activity could involve exploring decimals on a number line, drawn either on the board or on a computer. Encourage pupils to suggest numbers that lie between two of the numbers shown. Discuss how, when comparing decimals, it sometimes helps to add zero(s) so that all the decimals have the same number of decimal places: for example, to compare 0.03 and 0.029, write them as 0.030 and 0.029.

The questions in part C examine brain size, and involve the brain masses of four people, including Einstein and the novelist, Ivan Turgenev. Discuss the fact that, despite being thought of as very intelligent, Einstein's brain mass was not as great as others, and was in fact smaller than average. These four masses can also be compared with the brain masses of animals. Discuss whether this information shows a correlation between size of animal and brain mass.

Pages 14 & 15

It is important that pupils begin to appreciate the highest and lowest possible numbers that round to a given number, e.g. a number that has been rounded to 1000 to the nearest 10 could be any number between 995 and 1004. Demonstrate this by drawing a line on the board and writing 1000 in the centre. Since this is rounding to the nearest ten we must look for numbers up to 5 either side. Remind pupils that 5s round up, so 1004 is the highest number as 1005 will round up to 1010. Then ask pupils to suggest the highest and lowest number if this was rounded to the nearest 100 (950 and 1049) and to the nearest 1000 (500 and 1499).

Integers, powers and roots

Pages 18 & 19

The idea of adding or subtracting a negative number is a difficult one. Rather than just teaching a rule, spend some time discussing how to subtract a debt, i.e. to add the amount owed: for example, *You owe me £10. You want to get rid of your debt (subtract a negative), so you must pay that amount to me (add it).* Such contexts can help pupils to understand a reason for the rule, and also help them to remember it more effectively. The pupils will require calculators for checking their answers to part A. Discuss the sign change key, and how it is shown on different calculators: +/– or (–). Demonstrate how to key in a question such as 17 – ¯38 or 14 + ¯43 using the sign change key. Ensure pupils realise that in these examples the first sign is the operation of addition or subtraction, and the second sign denotes a negative number. Be aware that some calculators require the sign change key to be pressed *after*, rather than before the number.

Pages 20 & 21

These pages explore the relationship between positive and negative numbers, and examine multiplying and dividing negative numbers by continuing patterns from positive to negative. As a mental oral activity, hold up two ¯4 cards and ask: I have two lots of negative four, how much do I have? Write this as 2 x ¯4. Repeat for other multiples of ¯4. Next hold up four cards showing ¯2 and write this as 4 x ¯2. Encourage pupils to generalise that when one number is a negative, the answer will be negative.

Pages 22 & 23

During the first part of the lesson, find out which tests of divisibility the pupils already know: for example, *a number is divisible by 9 if the sum of its digits is a multiple of 9.* Discuss other tests of divisibility and write numbers on the board for pupils to test.

Pages 24 & 25

In the first part of the lesson, demonstrate how to find prime factors of numbers. Firstly, discuss and list prime numbers, particularly those below 10, i.e. 2, 3, 5 and 7. Make some numbers by multiplying the prime numbers together: for example, 30 can be made by 2 x 3 x 5, or 24 by 2 x 2 x 2 x 3. Explain that these prime numbers are known as **prime factors** – numbers that divide exactly into the number 30 or 24.

The activities on the second page encourage pupils to use prime factors to find the highest common factor (HCF) and the lowest common multiples (LCM). Discuss with pupils the text at the foot of the page and provide examples to assist them: for example find the HCF and LCM of the numbers

12, 16 and 28. Ask pupils to list the prime factors: $12 = 2 \times 2 \times 3$, $16 = 2 \times 2 \times 2 \times 2$, $28 = 2 \times 2 \times 7$. The shared factors are 2×2 or 2^2 so the HCF is 4. To find the LCM, write the prime factors using indices: $12 = 2^2 \times 3$, $16 = 2^4$, $28 = 2^2 \times 7$. Look at each prime factor in turn and choose those with the highest powers, to give $2^4 \times 3 \times 7 = 336$. Remind pupils that the LCM is useful when adding and subtracting fractions with different denominators. For example $\frac{1}{12} + \frac{3}{16} + \frac{5}{28}$ can be found by changing each fraction to an equivalent one with the LCM as the denominator: $\frac{28}{336} + \frac{63}{336} + \frac{60}{336} = \frac{151}{336}$.

Pages 26 & 27

Watch out for pupils confusing doubling with squaring. Give plenty of examples in the first part of the lesson, for example $4^2 = 4 \times 4 = 16$ (not 8).

Fractions, decimals, percentages, ratio and proportion

Pages 38 & 39

Demonstrate to pupils how, when adding fractions with different denominators, it is first necessary to change the fractions so that they have the same denominator. To find which new denominator to use, find the lowest common multiple (LCM) of the existing denominators, then change each fraction to an equivalent one with the LCM as the denominator.

The LCM can sometimes be found by looking at the numbers and seeing which is the lowest number into which they will all divide. For more difficult sets of numbers, e.g. $\frac{1}{12} + \frac{3}{16} + \frac{5}{28}$ show pupils how to write each denominator as its prime factors: $12 = 2^2 \times 3$, $16 = 2^4$, $28 = 2^2 \times 7$. Look at each prime factor in turn and choose those with the highest powers, to give $2^4 \times 3 \times 7 = 336$. Then convert each fraction into an equivalent one with the LCM as the denominator and simply add the numerators: $\frac{28}{336} + \frac{63}{336} + \frac{60}{336} = \frac{15}{336}$.

Pages 40 & 41

Remind pupils that when adding and subtracting fractions they should be careful not to add or subtract the denominators as well as the numerators. For example, $\frac{1}{5} + \frac{3}{5}$ is not $\frac{4}{10}$ but $\frac{4}{5}$. Explain that it is necessary for fractions to have the same denominator before the numerators can be added or subtracted.

Pages 42 & 43

Discuss the text at the foot of page 42. This explains two different methods for multiplying a fraction by

an integer. Where the numbers allow, pupils can divide the integer by the denominator of the fraction. For example $\frac{3}{5}$ of 35 can be found by first dividing 35 by 5, to give you one fifth of 35. To find three fifths, multiply the answer by three. The second method is necessary where the integer is not a multiple of the denominator: for example $\frac{4}{5}$ of 12. Here, multiply the numerator by the integer to find how many fifths there are altogether ($4 \times 12 = 48$ so there are 48 fifths). This can then be changed to a mixed number: $9\frac{3}{5}$.

Pages 44 & 45

These pages explore dividing an integer by a fraction. Encourage pupils to ask: *How many of this fraction is there in this number?* For example, for $15 \div \frac{1}{3}$ they should think: *How many thirds are there in 15? There are 3 thirds in one whole, so there must be 3×15 in 15 wholes. $3 \times 15 = 45$.*

Pages 46 & 47

At the start of the lesson, discuss different ways of finding percentages in your head. Pupils will have a variety of strategies, all of which may be valid providing they consistently give a correct answer. 75%, for example, can be found by halving the number to give 50% and halving the answer to give 25% and then (a) adding the two answers or (b) multiplying the answer for 25% by three or (c) subtracting the answer for 25% from the original number. Discuss other strategies and encourage pupils to demonstrate their methods on the board.

Pages 52 & 53

Note that there are several different ways of calculating percentage increases. Encourage pupils to use other methods and see whether they get the same answer: for example, to increase a number by 15%, simply multiply by 115% (or 1.15).

Pages 56 & 57

Begin the lesson by revising ratio as a comparison between **two** parts of a whole, written using a colon, for example 6 : 3. Demonstrate how to change ratios into their simplest form, for example 6 : 3 → 2 : 1. As pupils tend to find this a difficult concept, they will benefit from many examples in context, such as parts of blackcurrant juice to water, or parts of sand to cement in a mix.

Pupils often experience great difficulty understanding the difference between ratio and proportion. Encourage them to think of proportion as a fraction, decimal or percentage, and of ratio as a comparison between two or more parts of a whole, written using a colon, for example 3 : 2. Ratio compares part with part, while proportion compares a part with the whole. Pupils may need many examples in context before this is fully understood.

Power to the people

1. Multiply each number by 10. Write the answer in figures and words.

	B	HM	TM	M	HTh	TTh	Th	H	T	U	
(a)									1	0	
								1	*0*	*0*	*one hundred*
(b)								1	0	0	
(c)							1	0	0	0	
(d)						1	0	0	0	0	
(e)					1	0	0	0	0	0	
(f)				1	0	0	0	0	0	0	
(g)			1	0	0	0	0	0	0	0	
(h)		1	0	0	0	0	0	0	0	0	

2. Using only the number 10 and the × sign, make questions which have these answers:

(a) 100   *10 × 10* _____   **(b)** 1000 _____

(c) 10 000 _____   **(d)** 100 000 _____

What do you notice? _____

B

Continue this pattern.

(a) one hundred = _____ *100 = 10 × 10* _____ = 10^2

(b) one thousand = _____ *1 000 = 10 × 10 × 10* _____ = 10^3

(c) ten thousand = _____ *10 000* = _____ = _____

(d) one hundred thousand = _____ = _____ = _____

(e) one million = _____ = _____ = _____

(f) ten million = _____ = _____ = _____

(g) one hundred million = _____ = _____ = _____

(h) one billion = _____ = _____ = _____

One thousand million is called one billion. One million has six zeros (1 000 000) and one billion has nine zeros (1 000 000 000). Did you know that there are 100 billion cells in your brain?!

Power to the people

C

1. Here is a shorthand way of writing large numbers.
   Write out the multiplication and write the number in full.

   (a) 3×10^6 = *3 x 1 000 000 = 3 000 000*

   (b) 5×10^6 = _____

   (c) 8×10^5 = _____

   (d) 9×10^7 = _____

   (e) 1.5×10^6 = _____

   (f) 3.4×10^3 = _____

   (g) 8.2×10^4 = _____

2. Write the number in full for each statement.

   (a)

   I have been alive for approximately 7×10^8 seconds.
   700 000 000

   (b)
   I have been alive for approximately 7×10^7 seconds.
   _____

   (c)
   I have been alive for approximately 1.8×10^9 seconds.
   _____
   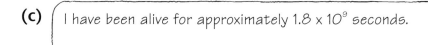

   (d)
   I have been alive for approximately 4.2×10^8 seconds.
   _____

3. Make eight different numbers using these cards. Write the numbers out in full.

   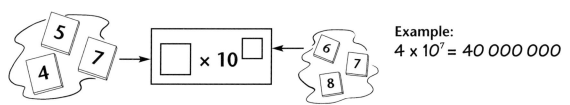

   Example:
   $4 \times 10^7 = 40\ 000\ 000$

NOW TRY THIS!

● 🖩 Work out approximately how old you are in:

(a) days _____ **(b)** hours _____

(c) minutes _____ **(d)** seconds _____

💡 Remember how to say these numbers aloud. 3×10^3 means 'three times **ten to the power three**'. It is not the same as 3^3 which means 'three cubed' or 'three times three times three'.

Developing Numeracy
Numbers and the Number System
Year 8
© A & C BLACK

9

Decimal dilemmas

 A

1. Use a calculator to find the answers.

    (a) $6 \times 0.1 = $ _0.6_   **(b)** $7 \times 0.1 = $ _____   **(c)** $15 \times 0.1 = $ _____

    (d) $20 \times 0.1 = $ _____   **(e)** $50 \times 0.1 = $ _____   **(f)** $92 \times 0.1 = $ _____

2. Find these answers without using a calculator.

    (a) $6 \div 10 = $ _0.6_   **(b)** $7 \div 10 = $ _____   **(c)** $15 \div 10 = $ _____

    (d) $20 \div 10 = $ _____   **(e)** $50 \div 10 = $ _____   **(f)** $92 \div 10 = $ _____

3. What do you notice about **multiplying by 0.1** and **dividing by 10**?

    _____

4. Use a calculator to find the answers.

    (a) $6 \times 0.01 = $ _____   **(b)** $7 \times 0.01 = $ _____   **(c)** $15 \times 0.01 = $ _____

5. Find these answers without using a calculator.

    (a) $6 \div 100 = $ _____   **(b)** $7 \div 100 = $ _____   **(c)** $15 \div 100 = $ _____

6. What do you notice about **multiplying by 0.01** and **dividing by 100**?

    _____

7.

Find out what happens to a number when you **divide by 0.1**. What multiplication gives the same answer?

8.

Find out what happens to a number when you **divide by 0.01**. What multiplication gives the same answer?

 B Work out the answers in your head.

> Remember: one-tenth $\left(\frac{1}{10}\right)$ is equivalent to 0.1, and one-hundredth $\left(\frac{1}{100}\right)$ is equivalent to 0.01.

!

(a) $60 \times \frac{1}{10} = $ _____   **(b)** $27 \times \frac{1}{100} = $ _____

(c) $63 \div \frac{1}{10} = $ _____   **(d)** $8 \div \frac{1}{100} = $ _____   **(e)** $34 \times \frac{1}{10} = $ _____

(f) $45 \times \frac{1}{100} = $ _____   **(g)** $51 \div \frac{1}{10} = $ _____   **(h)** $73 \div \frac{1}{100} = $ _____

When you multiply decimals by 10, the digits move one place to the left $(3.14 \times 10 = 31.4)$. When you multiply decimals by 100, the digits move two places to the left $(3.14 \times 100 = 314)$. When you divide by 10 or 100, the digits move one or two places to the right $(3.14 \div 100 = 0.0314)$.

Developing Numeracy
Numbers and the Number System
Year 8
© A & C BLACK

Decimal dilemmas

C

1. Is each statement true or false?

Write three examples to prove this.

$5 \times 0.01 = 0.05$

(a) Multiplying by 0.01 makes a number smaller.

True ✓
False

(b) Dividing always makes a number smaller.

True
False

(c) Dividing by one-tenth makes a number larger.

True
False

(d) Dividing by 0.1 gives the same answer as multiplying by 10.

True
False

(e) When you multiply a positive whole number by a number less than one, the answer is always larger.

True
False

(f) When you divide a positive whole number by a number less than one, the answer is always larger.

True
False

2. Choose four different starting numbers and follow these trails. Show your workings.

Start | × 0.1 | × 0.1 | ÷ 0.01 | ÷ 0.01 | **Finish**

Start | ÷ 10 | ÷ 10 | × 100 | × 100 | **Finish**

What do you notice? _____

NOW TRY THIS!

● Use these cards to make three pairs of multiplication and division questions. The questions in each pair must have the same answer.

Example: $0.5 \times 10 = 5$
$0.5 \div \frac{1}{10} = 5$

| 0.5 |
| 5 |

| × |
| ÷ |

100	0.1
10	0.01
$\frac{1}{10}$	$\frac{1}{100}$

You can use a calculator to check that each question you have written on this page has the correct answer. Remember that one-tenth is equivalent to 0.1 and one-hundredth is equivalent to 0.01.

Brain strain

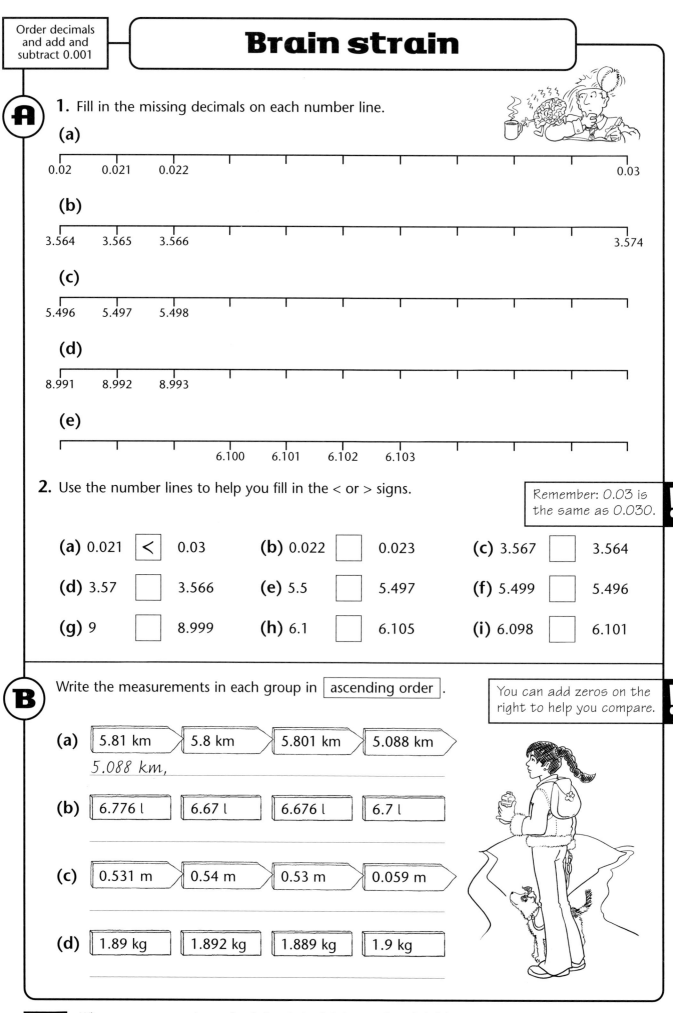

A 1. Fill in the missing decimals on each number line.

(a)

0.02   0.021   0.022   0.03

(b)

3.564   3.565   3.566   3.574

(c)

5.496   5.497   5.498

(d)

8.991   8.992   8.993

(e)

                              6.100   6.101   6.102   6.103

2. Use the number lines to help you fill in the < or > signs.

> **!** Remember: 0.03 is the same as 0.030.

(a) 0.021 `<` 0.03   **(b)** 0.022 ☐ 0.023   **(c)** 3.567 ☐ 3.564

(d) 3.57 ☐ 3.566   **(e)** 5.5 ☐ 5.497   **(f)** 5.499 ☐ 5.496

(g) 9 ☐ 8.999   **(h)** 6.1 ☐ 6.105   **(i)** 6.098 ☐ 6.101

B Write the measurements in each group in ⟨ ascending order ⟩.

> **!** You can add zeros on the right to help you compare.

(a) ⟩5.81 km⟩ ⟩5.8 km⟩ ⟩5.801 km⟩ ⟩5.088 km⟩

_5.088 km,_

(b) ⟨6.776 l⟩ ⟨6.67 l⟩ ⟨6.676 l⟩ ⟨6.7 l⟩

(c) ⟩0.531 m⟩ ⟩0.54 m⟩ ⟩0.53 m⟩ ⟩0.059 m⟩

(d) ⟨1.89 kg⟩ ⟨1.892 kg⟩ ⟨1.889 kg⟩ ⟨1.9 kg⟩

When you are comparing and ordering decimals it is sometimes helpful to write the decimals in columns, lining up the decimal points. Then compare the digits in each column, starting with the column furthest to the left. **Ascending order** means in order from smallest to largest.

Developing Numeracy Numbers and the Number System Year 8 © A & C BLACK

Brain strain

C

Here are the masses of four people's brains.

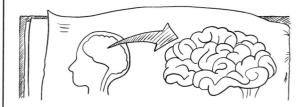

Einstein's brain	(male)	1.37 kg
Turgenev's brain	(male)	2.02 kg
Gambettan's brain	(male)	1.294 kg
Millbrook's brain	(female)	1.7 kg

1. Which of the four people above has the:

(a) heaviest brain? _____ **(b)** lightest brain? _____

2. If the average human brain weighs 1.4 kg, which of the brains are heavier than average?

_____

Here are the masses of some animal brains.

baboon	0.14 kg	racoon	0.039 kg
whale	10 kg	monkey	0.1 kg
kangaroo	0.056 kg	camel	0.68 kg
dolphin	1.7 kg	cat	0.03 kg

elephant 4.999 kg
rabbit 0.012 kg

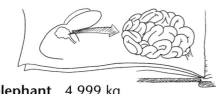

3. (a) List the animal brain masses in order, starting with the heaviest.

10 kg, _____

(b) Which animal brains are heavier than the average human brain of 1.4 kg?

_____

(c) Which animal brains are lighter than the average human baby's brain of 0.35 kg?

_____

(d) A rat's brain is one-sixth of the mass of a rabbit's. What is its mass? _____

NOW TRY THIS!

This statement is about a number called *b*.

$$42.62 \leq b \leq 42.82$$

> This means *b* is less than or equal to 42.82, and greater than or equal to 42.62.

!

● Write digits in the boxes to show different numbers that *b* could stand for.

4	2 .		
4	2 .		
4	2 .			

4	2 .	
4	2 .	
4	2 .		

For the 'Now try this!' challenge, you might find it helpful to draw a number line with 42.62 and 42.82 at either end. Which numbers with one decimal place lie between them? Mark them on the number line first. Now think of numbers with two decimal places, and so on.

Round or about

A 1. Round each lottery win to the nearest 10, 100, 1000 and 10 000.

Go back to the original number each time before rounding.

Number	To nearest 10	To nearest 100	To nearest 1000	To nearest 10 000
£628 057	£628 060	£628 100	£628 000	£630 000
£512 781				
£405 452				
£816 724				
£554 519				
£813 894				
£161 982				
£759 915				
£199 899				
£247 999				
£749 999				
£499 999				

2. These two people are talking about the **same number** of computers sold. Explain how this can be true.

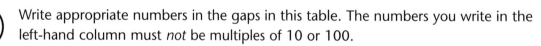

Our company has sold about one million computers.

Our company has sold about seven hundred thousand computers.

B Write appropriate numbers in the gaps in this table. The numbers you write in the left-hand column must *not* be multiples of 10 or 100.

Number	To nearest 10	To nearest 100	To nearest 1000	To nearest 10 000
784 078	784 080	784 100	784 000	780 000
	469 570	469 600		470 000
	986 550		987 000	
		109 500	110 000	110 000
		109 500	109 000	110 000
	150 000	150 000	150 000	150 000

When you round to the nearest ten, the answer will be a multiple of 10 (or zero). When you round to the nearest 100, the answer will be a multiple of 100 (or zero), and so on.

Developing Numeracy
Numbers and the Number System
Year 8
© A & C BLACK

Round or about

C

If you round to the nearest **1000**:
the lowest integer (whole number) that rounds to 46 000 is 45 500
and the highest integer that rounds to 46 000 is 46 499.

```
45 000              46 000              47 000
  |_____|_____|
            ↑                   ↑
        45 500              46 499
```

Find the lowest and highest integers that round to the following numbers.

(a) When rounded to the nearest **1000** it rounds to 34 000.

Lowest integer _____

Highest integer _____

(b) When rounded to the nearest **1000** it rounds to 20 000.

Lowest integer _____

Highest integer _____

(c) When rounded to the nearest **100** it rounds to 22 700.

Lowest integer _____

Highest integer _____

(d) When rounded to the nearest **100** it rounds to 55 900.

Lowest integer _____

Highest integer _____

(e) When rounded to the nearest **10 000** it rounds to 20 000.

Lowest integer _____

Highest integer _____

(f) When rounded to the nearest **10 000** it rounds to 80 000.

Lowest integer _____

Highest integer _____

(g) When rounded to the nearest **100** it rounds to 67 000.

Lowest integer _____

Highest integer _____

(h) When rounded to the nearest **10** it rounds to 10 000.

Lowest integer _____

Highest integer _____

NOW TRY THIS!

● What are the highest and lowest integers that Lucy could be thinking of?

I'm thinking of a number that when rounded to the nearest 1000 is 45 000...

...and when rounded to the nearest 10 000 is 50 000.

Lowest integer _____

Highest integer _____

Take note of whether the number has been rounded to the nearest 10, 100, 1000, and so on. In the example at the top of the page you are rounding to the nearest 1000, so you can find the lowest integer by subtracting half of 1000 from 46 000 (45 500). Find the highest integer by adding one less than the amount you subtracted (46 499).

**Developing Numeracy
Numbers and the Number System
Year 8**
© A & C BLACK

Round decimals to the nearest whole number or 1 or 2 d.p.

Recurring nightmares!

A Divide each number in the first column by **16**. Write the answer shown on the calculator display. Then round it to the nearest whole number, and to one and two decimal places.

> ! Go back to the original number each time before rounding.

Number	Calculator display	To nearest whole number	To one decimal place	To two decimal places
757	47.3125	47	47.3	47.31
547				
4 583				
5 489				
7 149				
8 451				
7 898				
4 555				
12 638				
127.59				
14.86				
15.92				

B **1.** Divide the number **1** by 2, 3, 4, 5, 6, 7, 8, 9, 10, 11, and 12. Write the questions and answers in the correct boxes below.

> ! Some answers will be recurring decimals, others will not.

Non-recurring decimal answers

1 ÷ 2 = 0.5

Recurring decimal answers

1 ÷ 3 = 0.3333333

2. Now write each recurring decimal to one decimal place (to 1 d.p.).

0.3333333 = 0.3 to 1 d.p.

Recurring decimals are decimals where digits are repeated. We often put a dot above the repeating digits to show they recur, for example 0.3333333 can be written as 0.3 (with a dot above the 3). Note that 1 ÷ 7 is a recurring decimal where the digits 142857 are repeated.

16

**Developing Numeracy
Numbers and the Number System
Year 8
© A & C BLACK**

Recurring nightmares!

C

1. Find some recurring decimals produced by dividing one-digit and two-digit integers by 9.

☐ 7 ÷ 9 = 0.7777777 = _0.8_ to 1 d.p.

☐ ☐ ÷ 9 = ☐ = _____ to 1 d.p.

☐ ☐ ÷ 9 = ☐ = _____ to 1 d.p.

☐ ☐ ÷ 9 = ☐ = _____ to 1 d.p.

☐ ☐ ÷ 9 = ☐ = _____ to 1 d.p.

☐ ☐ ÷ 9 = ☐ = _____ to 1 d.p.

Write what you notice about dividing by 9. _____

_____

I'm having a recurring nightmare.

2. Now divide some one-digit integers by 11.

☐ ÷ **11** = ☐ = _____ to 2 d.p.

☐ ÷ **11** = ☐ = _____ to 2 d.p.

☐ ÷ **11** = ☐ = _____ to 2 d.p.

☐ ÷ **11** = ☐ = _____ to 2 d.p.

☐ ÷ **11** = ☐ = _____ to 2 d.p.

☐ ÷ **11** = ☐ = _____ to 2 d.p.

Write what you notice about dividing by 11. _____

_____

Say that again?

NOW TRY THIS!

- Investigate the recurring decimals produced when you divide one-digit and two-digit integers by 6. Round each answer to one or two decimal places.

  Example: 1 7 ÷ 6 = 2.8333333 = _2.83_ to 2 d.p.

  2 0 ÷ 6 = 3.3333333 = _3.3_ to 1 d.p.

- Describe the patterns you notice when dividing by 6. _____

_____

Remember that an **integer** is a positive or negative whole number. As a further challenge, see what happens when you divide one-digit and two-digit integers by 12.

Developing Numeracy Numbers and the Number System Year 8 © A & C BLACK

17

Total difference

A

1. Answer these addition and subtraction questions.

Subtracting ← → Adding

$^{-}10$ $^{-}9$ $^{-}8$ $^{-}7$ $^{-}6$ $^{-}5$ $^{-}4$ $^{-}3$ $^{-}2$ $^{-}1$ **0** 1 2 3 4 5 6 7 8 9 10

> **!** Remember: when adding, move in a positive direction. When subtracting, move in a negative direction.

(a) $9 - 17$ = $^{-}8$

(b) $^{-}8 + 13$ = _____

(c) $^{-}7 - 13$ = _____

(d) $^{-}20 + 14$ = _____

(e) $^{-}7 - 34$ = _____

(f) $^{-}24 + 46$ = _____

(g) $26 - 37$ = _____

(h) $51 + ^{-}26$ = _____

(i) $^{-}17 - ^{-}38$ = _____

(j) $^{-}13 + 25$ = _____

(k) $^{-}99 - ^{-}23$ = _____

(l) $21 + ^{-}39$ = _____

2. Answer these questions. Rewrite them to help you.

> **!** Think of subtracting a negative as 'add', and adding a negative as 'subtract'.

(a) $15 - ^{-}14 = 29$
    $15 + 14 = 29$

(b) $^{-}7 + ^{-}8 = ^{-}15$
    $^{-}7 - 8 = ^{-}15$

(c) $22 - ^{-}15 =$

(d) $^{-}50 - ^{-}63 =$

(e) $^{-}24 + ^{-}46 =$

(f) $46 - ^{-}37 =$

(g) $51 + ^{-}37 =$

(h) $^{-}17 - ^{-}38 =$

(i) $^{-}13 + ^{-}25 =$

(j) $^{-}99 - ^{-}46 =$

(k) $21 + ^{-}42 =$

3. Check all your answers with a calculator.
Use the sign change key.

B

Fill in the missing integers so that each pair has a total of zero.

(a) $^{-}4 + \boxed{4} = 0$

(b) $\boxed{} + 8 = 0$

(c) $^{-}16 + \boxed{} = 0$

(d) $7 + \boxed{} = 0$

(e) $\boxed{} + ^{-}9 = 0$

(f) $\boxed{} + ^{-}3 = 0$

(g) $^{-}14 + \boxed{} = 0$

(h) $\boxed{} + ^{-}27 = 0$

(i) $12 + \boxed{} = 0$

Make sure you know which is the **sign change** key on your calculator. On some calculators it shows +/− and on others it shows (−). Ask your teacher if you are not sure. Remember that an **integer** is a positive or negative whole number.

Developing Numeracy
Numbers and the Number System
Year 8
© A & C BLACK

Total difference

☆ The key below shows which letters stand for which numbers.
☆ Add up the values of the letters to find the total value of a word.

Example: LOST = 24 + ⁻10 + ⁻5 + 40 = 49

1. Write as many words as you can with more than three letters which have:
   (a) a total value of zero   (b) a total value of between ⁻20 and ⁻25

2. What is the total value of your name? _____

3. Make a word with as large a value as you can.

Record your words and their totals here.

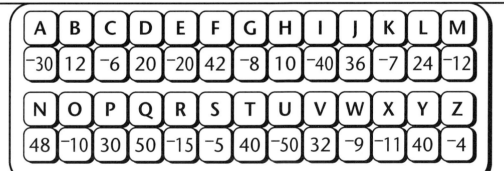

Key:

A	B	C	D	E	F	G	H	I	J	K	L	M
⁻30	12	⁻6	20	⁻20	42	⁻8	10	⁻40	36	⁻7	24	⁻12

N	O	P	Q	R	S	T	U	V	W	X	Y	Z
48	⁻10	30	50	⁻15	⁻5	40	⁻50	32	⁻9	⁻11	40	⁻4

● Using the key above, find the **difference** between these pairs of letters.

H	I	$10 - ⁻40 = 50$		A	T

O	F			M	A

● Find the difference for other pairs of letters.

Think of subtracting a negative as 'add' and think of adding a negative as 'subtract'. When finding the difference between two numbers, think of this as a subtraction question.

Developing Numeracy
Numbers and the Number System
Year 8
© A & C BLACK

Positive or negative?

A

1. 🏚 Complete these tables. Write what you notice about multiplying **negative** numbers.

(a)

5 × 2	4 × 2	3 × 2	2 × 2	1 × 2	0 × 2	⁻1 × 2	⁻2 × 2	⁻3 × 2	⁻4 × 2	⁻5 × 2
10										

(b)

5 × ⁻2	4 × ⁻2	3 × ⁻2	2 × ⁻2	1 × ⁻2	0 × ⁻2	⁻1 × ⁻2	⁻2 × ⁻2	⁻3 × ⁻2	⁻4 × ⁻2	⁻5 × ⁻2
⁻10										

2. 🏚 Now answer these questions.

   (a) ⁻6 × 2 = _⁻12_   **(b)** ⁻8 × 2 = _____   **(c)** ⁻9 × 2   = _____

   (d) 8 × ⁻2 = _____   **(e)** ⁻6 × ⁻2 = _____   **(f)** ⁻7 × ⁻2 = _____

   (g) ⁻15 × 2 = _____   **(h)** 14 × ⁻2 = _____   **(i)** ⁻50 × ⁻2 = _____

3. 🖩 Check all your answers with a calculator. Use the **sign change** key.

B

Complete this multiplication square. Colour the **positive** answers yellow.

×	⁻3	⁻2	⁻1	0	1	2	3
3	⁻9			0			
2							
1							
0							
⁻1							
⁻2							
⁻3							

POSITIVE OR NEGATIVE, SIR?

Make sure you know which is the **sign change** key on your calculator. On some calculators it shows +/− and on others it shows (−). Ask your teacher if you are not sure.

Developing Numeracy
Numbers and the Number System
Year 8
© A & C BLACK

Positive or negative?

1. Answer these multiplication and division questions.

(a) ⁻6 × 3 = _____   (b) ⁻6 × ⁻3 = _____   (c) 6 × ⁻3 = _____

(d) 6 ÷ ⁻3 = _____   (e) ⁻6 ÷ ⁻3 = _____   (f) ⁻6 ÷ 3 = _____

2. Look for a pattern in your answers. Write rules about what happens when you multiply or divide numbers with the same sign, and numbers with different signs.

_____

_____

3. Play this game with a partner. You each need a coloured pencil and a calculator.

☆ Take turns to choose two numbers from the vampire's napkin. (Choose carefully!)
☆ *Without* using a calculator, multiply or divide one number by the other.
   Your partner uses a calculator to check your answer.
☆ If the answer is correct and appears in the grid, colour this square using your colour.
☆ Record your question and answer below.
☆ The winner is the first player to colour four squares in a line.

⁻36	2	⁻0.5	⁻6.6	36	18
⁻4	⁻48	0.25	⁻9	0.5	⁻3
⁻0.25	⁻18	⁻24	6	⁻2	8
⁻4.5	⁻6	⁻1.3	12	⁻1.5	9
4.5	⁻12	4	⁻1	72	⁻2.6
2	⁻18	⁻2	1	⁻0.75	⁻0.5

STEAK, SIR?

⁻6   ⁻12   4   ⁻3   3   ⁻1.5   2

Questions and answers

NOW TRY THIS!

● Write at least ten different multiplication or division questions with the answer ⁻36.

   Example: 9 × ⁻4 = ⁻36

Remember that division questions can be written as fractions, so ⁻6 ÷ 3 can be written as $\frac{⁻6}{3}$. Note that $\frac{⁻6}{3}$ and $\frac{6}{⁻3}$ have the same answer (⁻2). In the grid game, your lines can be horizontal, vertical or diagonal.

Testing times

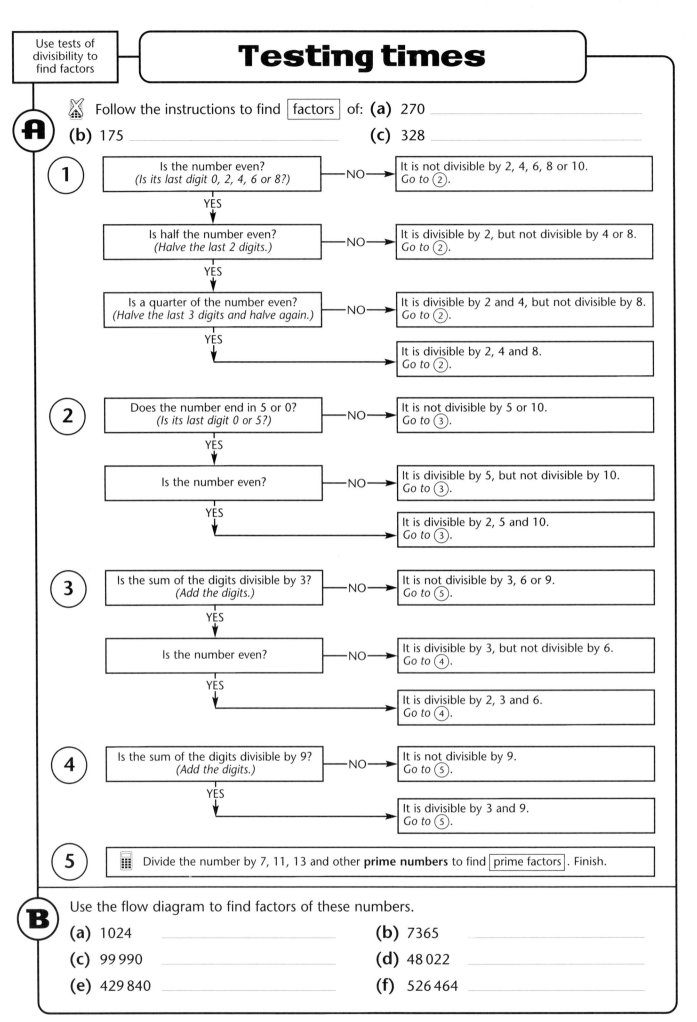

A

Follow the instructions to find ⬚factors⬚ of: **(a)** 270 _____

(b) 175 _____   **(c)** 328 _____

1

| Is the number even?
(Is its last digit 0, 2, 4, 6 or 8?) | —NO→ | It is not divisible by 2, 4, 6, 8 or 10.
Go to ② . |

YES ↓

| Is half the number even?
(Halve the last 2 digits.) | —NO→ | It is divisible by 2, but not divisible by 4 or 8.
Go to ② . |

YES ↓

| Is a quarter of the number even?
(Halve the last 3 digits and halve again.) | —NO→ | It is divisible by 2 and 4, but not divisible by 8.
Go to ② . |

YES ↓

| It is divisible by 2, 4 and 8.
Go to ② . |

2

| Does the number end in 5 or 0?
(Is its last digit 0 or 5?) | —NO→ | It is not divisible by 5 or 10.
Go to ③ . |

YES ↓

| Is the number even? | —NO→ | It is divisible by 5, but not divisible by 10.
Go to ③ . |

YES ↓

| It is divisible by 2, 5 and 10.
Go to ③ . |

3

| Is the sum of the digits divisible by 3?
(Add the digits.) | —NO→ | It is not divisible by 3, 6 or 9.
Go to ⑤ . |

YES ↓

| Is the number even? | —NO→ | It is divisible by 3, but not divisible by 6.
Go to ④ . |

YES ↓

| It is divisible by 2, 3 and 6.
Go to ④ . |

4

| Is the sum of the digits divisible by 9?
(Add the digits.) | —NO→ | It is not divisible by 9.
Go to ⑤ . |

YES ↓

| It is divisible by 3 and 9.
Go to ⑤ . |

5

Divide the number by 7, 11, 13 and other **prime numbers** to find ⬚prime factors⬚ . Finish.

B

Use the flow diagram to find factors of these numbers.

(a) 1024 _____   **(b)** 7365 _____

(c) 99 990 _____   **(d)** 48 022 _____

(e) 429 840 _____   **(f)** 526 464 _____

A **factor** is a number that divides exactly into another without a remainder.
A **prime number** has only two factors, itself and 1. Here are the first ten
prime numbers: 2, 3, 5, 7, 11, 13, 17, 19, 23, 29. A **prime factor** is a
factor that is a prime number. The next sheet will show you how to find
other factors using those you have already found.

Developing Numeracy
Numbers and the Number System
Year 8
© A & C BLACK

Testing times

C

- If a number has the factors 3 and 4, it also has the factor 12.
- If a number has the factors 3 and 5, it also has the factor 15.
- If a number has the factors 2 and 9, it also has the factor 18.

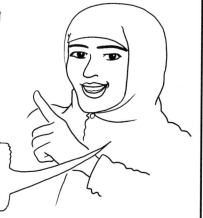

1116 has the factors 2, 3, 4, 6 and 9.
The factors 3 and 4 tell me it has the factor 12,
and the factors 2 and 9 tell me it has the factor 18.

1. Use the rules above to find out whether these numbers have the factors 12, 15 or 18.
Circle the number if it is a factor.

(a) 1020   (12)   (15)   18   (b) 7365   12   15   18

(c) 31 656   12   15   18   (d) 73 737   12   15   18

(e) 99 990   12   15   18   (f) 48 042   12   15   18

(g) 429 840   12   15   18   (h) 526 464   12   15   18

2. Tick or cross to show who is telling the truth.

(a)
18 is a common factor
of 99 990 and 73 737.

☐

(b)
15 is a common factor
of 99 990 and 429 840.

☐

(c)
18 is a common factor
of 99 990 and 48 042.

☐

(d)
12 is a common factor
of 48 042 and 429 840.

☐

(e)
15 is a common factor
of 99 990 and 7365.

☐

(f)
12 is a common factor
of 1020 and 526 464.

☐

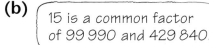

NOW TRY THIS!

- Circle the numbers below which are *not* factors of:

6 894 720

2   3   4   5   6   7   8   9   10   11   12   13   14   15   16   17   18   19   20   21   22   23   24

 When two numbers share the same factor we say it is a **common factor**, for example 20 and 25 have a common factor of 5, as 5 is a factor of both.

Recognise and use
prime factors and
common factors

Factor facts

A

Factor trees help you to find all the **prime factors** of a number.

Start with the number in a circle.

Find a **prime factor**
and divide by it.

Continue dividing by
prime factors until you
are left with a prime number.

42

2   21

3   7

Always divide by the
lowest prime factor
you can.

!

prime number $42 = 2 \times 3 \times 7$

Find all the prime factors of these numbers.

(a)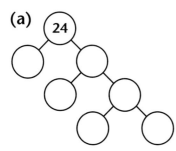

(b)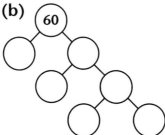

(c)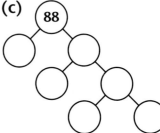

$24 =$ _____

(d)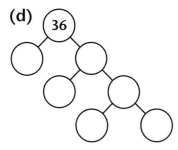

(e)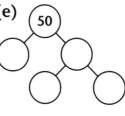

(f)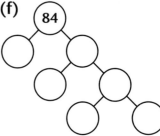

B   Rewrite these prime factor statements using powers where possible.

(a) $18 = 2 \times 3 \times 3 = \underline{2 \times 3^2}$ **(b)** $45 = 3 \times 3 \times 5 =$ _____

(c) $100 = 2 \times 2 \times 5 \times 5 =$ _____   **(d)** $108 = 2 \times 2 \times 3 \times 3 \times 3 =$ _____

(e) $140 = 2 \times 2 \times 5 \times 7 =$ _____   **(f)** $162 = 2 \times 3 \times 3 \times 3 \times 3 =$ _____

A **factor** is a number that divides exactly into another without a remainder.
A **prime factor** is a factor that is a prime number. A **prime number** has
only two factors, itself and 1. Here are the first ten prime numbers: 2, 3, 5,
7, 11, 13, 17, 19, 23, 29.

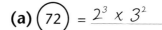

Factor facts

1. Write the prime factors of these numbers as multiplication statements using powers.

(a) (72) = $2^3 \times 3^2$ _____ **(b)** (54) = _____

(c) (120) = _____ **(d)** (156) = _____

(e) (240) = _____ **(f)** (450) = _____

(g) (686) = _____ **(h)** (294) = _____

(i) (324) = _____ **(j)** (378) = _____

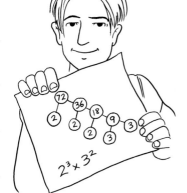

To find the | highest common factor | (HCF) of 72 and 54, compare the prime factors that both numbers share, in turn. Choose those with the lowest power and multiply them together. So: $2^3 \times 3^2$ and 2×3^3 **HCF is** $2 \times 3^2 = 18$

2. Using your answers to question 1, find the HCF of the numbers in these pairs.

(a) (120) and (156) _____ **(b)** (240) and (450) _____

(c) (686) and (294) _____ **(d)** (324) and (378) _____

To find the | lowest common multiple | (LCM) of 72 and 54, compare *all* the prime factors in turn. Choose those with the highest power and multiply them together.
So: $2^3 \times 3^2$ and 2×3^3 **LCM is** $2^3 \times 3^3 = 216$

3. Using your answers to question 1, find the LCM of the numbers in these pairs.

(a) (120) and (156) $2^3 \times 3 \times 5 \times 13 = 1560$ **(b)** (240) and (450) _____

(c) (686) and (294) _____ **(d)** (324) and (378) _____

NOW TRY THIS!

● Which numbers between 1 and 100 have only the prime factor:

(a) 2? _____ **(b)** 3? _____ **(c)** 5? _____

The **highest common factor** (HCF) is the highest number that divides into both numbers without a remainder: for example, the HCF of 12 and 8 is 4. The **lowest common multiple** (LCM) is the lowest number into which both numbers will divide without a remainder: for example, the LCM of 12 and 8 is 24.

Squares, cubes and roots

A **1.** Look at this book about □ square □ and □ cube □ numbers. Continue the pattern for other square and cube numbers. (Do not draw the shapes.)

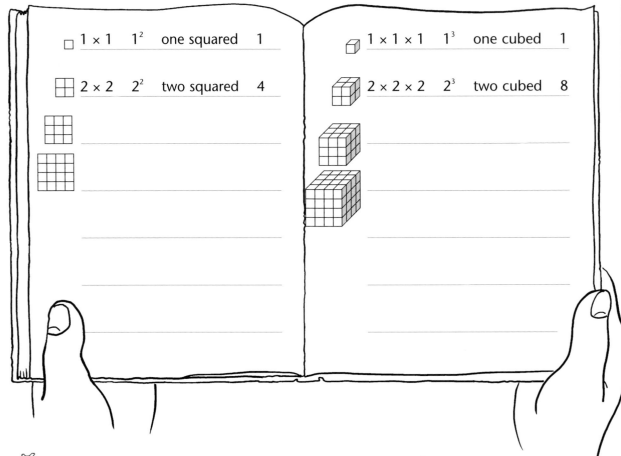

□ 1 × 1 1^2 one squared   1

□ 2 × 2 2^2 two squared   4

□ 1 × 1 × 1 1^3 one cubed   1

□ 2 × 2 × 2 2^3 two cubed   8

2. Write the value of these **square roots** ($\sqrt{\ }$) and **cube roots** ($\sqrt[3]{\ }$).

(a) $\sqrt{16}$ = 4

(b) $\sqrt{25}$ = ____

(c) $\sqrt{49}$ = ____

(d) $\sqrt{64}$ = ____

(e) $\sqrt{121}$ = ____

(f) $\sqrt{144}$ = ____

(g) $\sqrt[3]{8}$ = ____

(h) $\sqrt[3]{64}$ = ____

(i) $\sqrt[3]{27}$ = ____

(j) $\sqrt[3]{216}$ = ____

(k) $\sqrt[3]{343}$ = ____

(l) $\sqrt[3]{512}$ = ____

B **1.**  Find the value of these square numbers.

(a) $7^2 = 7 \times 7$ = ____

(b) $(^-7)^2 = {}^-7 \times {}^-7$ = ____

(c) $15^2 = 15 \times 15$ = ____

(d) $(^-15)^2 = {}^-15 \times {}^-15$ = ____

(e) $28^2 = 28 \times 28$ = ____

(f) $(^-28)^2 = {}^-28 \times {}^-28$ = ____

2. What do you notice? _____

_____

3. Give the two possible values of $\sqrt{64}$. $\sqrt{64}$ = ____ or ____

 To **square** a number, multiply the number by itself, or use the 'squaring' key on your calculator (often marked x^2). Try both ways. Finding the **square root** (the opposite) is finding which number has been multiplied by itself to get the given number. The square root key looks like this: $\boxed{\sqrt{\ }}$. To **cube** a number, multiply the number by itself and then by itself again.

Developing Numeracy
Numbers and the Number System
Year 8
© A & C BLACK

Squares, cubes and roots

1. Imagine that the square root key is broken on your calculator.

Without using the square root key, find the square root of these numbers. Show your workings in the boxes.

(a) 73.96

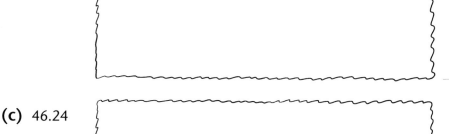

73.96 is between square numbers 64 and 81
8^2 = 64
9^2 = 81
8.5^2 = 72.25
8.6^2 = 73.96

$\sqrt{73.96}$ = 8.6

(b) 54.76

(c) 46.24

(d) 15.9201

2. Again, *without* using the square root key, find an **approximate** answer for the square root of 12. Give your answer to two decimal places (to 2 d.p.).

12

 Find the cube root of these numbers *without* using the $\sqrt[3]{}$ key.

(a) 17.576 _____   **(b)** 140.608 _____   **(c)** 25 (to 2 d.p.) _____

Remember that **squaring** means multiplying a number by itself, for example 4 × 4. So finding the **square root** (the opposite) is finding which number has been multiplied by itself to get the given number. When a number is **cubed** it is multiplied by itself twice, for example 4 × 4 × 4. The **cube root** is the opposite of this.

Square it, cube it

1. Join the equivalent cards in sets of three.

22³	17 × 17	484
17³	22 × 22 × 22	1225
35²	35 × 35 × 35	42 875
22²	17 × 17 × 17	289
35³	35 × 35	10 648
17²	22 × 22	4913

2. Mark this work and correct the mistakes.

(a) √324 = 18 ✓   (b) 45² = 2225   (c) ³√4913 = 17

(d) 64³ = 4   (e) 65³ = 274 625   (f) √71 824 = 268

(g) ³√300.763 = 6.7   (h) (0.1)² = 0.1   (i) (13.7)³ = 2571.353

Fill in the missing digits to make true statements.

(a) $\left(\boxed{1}\ \boxed{7} \right)^2 = \boxed{2}\ \boxed{8}\ \boxed{9}$ (b) $\left(\boxed{3}\ \boxed{} \right)^2 = \boxed{}\ \boxed{}\ \boxed{}$

(c) $\left(\boxed{}\ \boxed{9} \right)^2 = \boxed{}\ \boxed{4}\ \boxed{1}$ (d) $\left(\boxed{}\ \boxed{7} \right)^2 = \boxed{}\ \boxed{9}\ \boxed{}$

(e) $\left(\boxed{} \right)^3 = \boxed{}\ \boxed{1}\ \boxed{}$ (f) $\left(\boxed{}\ \boxed{} \right)^3 = \boxed{9}\ \boxed{}\ \boxed{}$

(g) $\left(\boxed{}\ \boxed{} \right)^3 = \boxed{}\ \boxed{}\ \boxed{}\ \boxed{5}$ (h) $\left(\boxed{}\ \boxed{} \right)^3 = \boxed{}\ \boxed{5}\ \boxed{}\ \boxed{}$

(i) $\left(\boxed{}\ \boxed{5} + \boxed{4}\ \boxed{} \right)^3 = \boxed{}\ \boxed{}\ \boxed{}\ \boxed{5}\ \boxed{0}\ \boxed{9}$

 Remember that **squaring** means multiplying a number by itself, for example 4 × 4. So finding the **square root** (the opposite) is finding which number has been multiplied by itself to get the given number. When a number is **cubed** it is multiplied by itself twice, for example 4 × 4 × 4. The **cube root** is the opposite of this.

**Developing Numeracy
Numbers and the Number System
Year 8
© A & C BLACK**

Square it, cube it

C Play this game with a partner. You each need a dice and a counter.

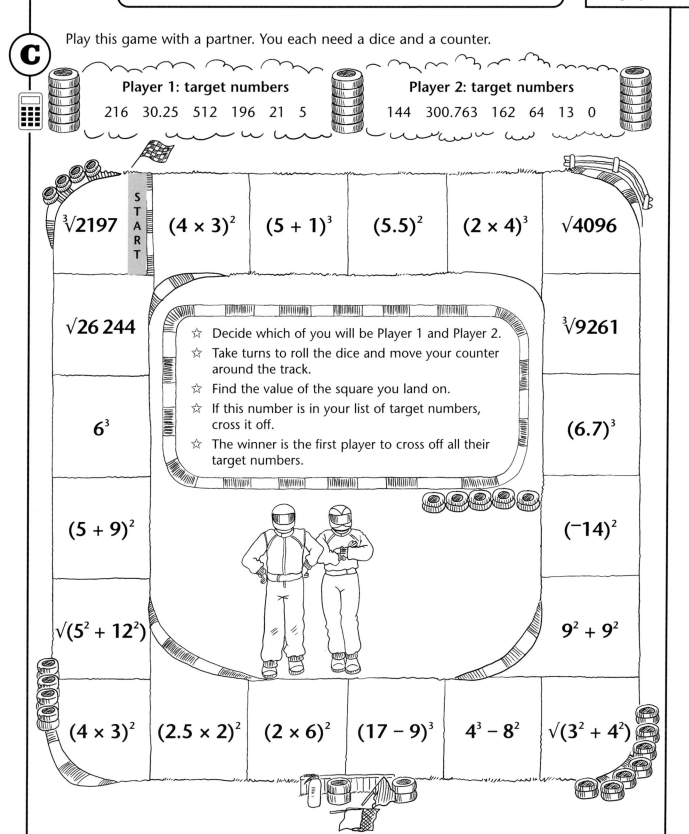

Player 1: target numbers
216 30.25 512 196 21 5

Player 2: target numbers
144 300.763 162 64 13 0

START

$\sqrt[3]{2197}$ $(4 \times 3)^2$ $(5 + 1)^3$ $(5.5)^2$ $(2 \times 4)^3$ $\sqrt{4096}$

$\sqrt{26\,244}$ $\sqrt[3]{9261}$

6^3 $(6.7)^3$

☆ Decide which of you will be Player 1 and Player 2.
☆ Take turns to roll the dice and move your counter around the track.
☆ Find the value of the square you land on.
☆ If this number is in your list of target numbers, cross it off.
☆ The winner is the first player to cross off all their target numbers.

$(5 + 9)^2$ $(^-14)^2$

$\sqrt{(5^2 + 12^2)}$ $9^2 + 9^2$

$(4 \times 3)^2$ $(2.5 \times 2)^2$ $(2 \times 6)^2$ $(17 - 9)^3$ $4^3 - 8^2$ $\sqrt{(3^2 + 4^2)}$

NOW TRY THIS!

● Find the value of these square numbers.

1^2 11^2 111^2 1111^2 11111^2

● Write what you notice about them and predict other numbers in the pattern.

 Remember to work out the part in brackets first, before squaring or cubing.
As a further challenge, investigate the pattern formed by squaring the numbers 9, 99, 999, 9999, and so on. Write what you notice.

Shape up

A Read this page from a booklet on semaphore. The flags create angles showing amount of clockwise turn.

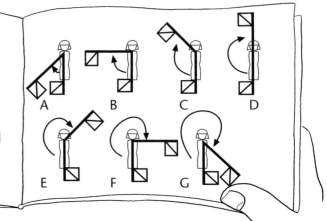

Semaphore

The semaphore signalling system is based on holding two flags.

The first seven letters of the alphabet are shown by one flag being extended and the other held vertically down.

1. **Estimate** what fraction of a complete turn is the angle shown for each letter. Write your answers in their simplest form.

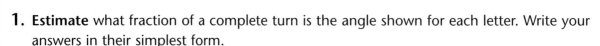

(a) A ____ $\frac{1}{8}$ ____   **(b)** B _____   **(c)** C _____   **(d)** D _____

(e) E _____   **(f)** F _____   **(g)** G _____

2. What fraction of a complete turn does the minute hand of a clock turn through between:

> **!** You'll need to write some of your answers as mixed numbers.

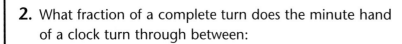

(a) 7:00 and 7:45? $\frac{45}{60} = \frac{3}{4}$ **(b)** 9:00 and 9:20? _____

(c) 8:40 and 8:45? _____   **(d)** 5:00 and 8:15? $3\frac{1}{4}$

(e) 5:10 and 6:40? _____   **(f)** 8:05 and 9:50? _____

(g) 4:40 and 6:45? _____   **(h)** 6:05 and 6:55? _____

(i) 2:10 and 7:00? _____   **(j)** 10:15 and 12:40? _____

(k) 3:20 and 5:55? _____   **(l)** 7:17 and 12:18? _____

B A floor is covered with 36 square carpet tiles.

(a) Shade the tiles so that:

$\frac{1}{6}$ are yellow

$\frac{2}{9}$ are red

$\frac{5}{12}$ are blue

$\frac{3}{18}$ are green

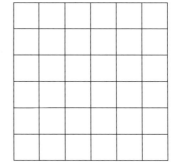

(b) What fraction of the floor is white? _____

Give all your answers as fractions in their simplest form. To do this, divide the **numerator** (top number) and the **denominator** (bottom number) by the same number until there is no other number that will divide exactly into both: for example $\frac{8}{20} = \frac{4}{10} = \frac{2}{5}$. A **mixed number** has a whole number part and a fraction part.

Developing Numeracy
Numbers and the Number System
Year 8
© A & C BLACK

Shape up

1. If you shade only whole triangles, can you shade exactly **three-quarters** of any of these shapes? Show your answer by colouring the shapes or leaving them blank.

Count the number of triangles in each shape first!

A   B   C   D   E   F

2. If you shade only whole triangles, can you shade exactly **two-thirds** of any of these shapes? Show your answer by colouring the shapes or leaving them blank.

   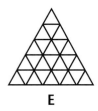 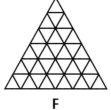

A   B   C   D   E   F

3. (a) If you shade only whole squares, can you shade exactly **eight-ninths** of any of these shapes? Show your answer by colouring the shapes or leaving them blank.

   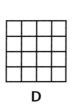 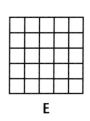 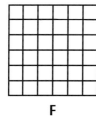

A   B   C   D   E   F

(b) What do you notice about the number of squares in the shapes directly above?

_____

(c) Predict the number of squares in the next four shapes in the pattern.

_____   _____   _____   _____

(d) Is it possible to shade eight-ninths of any of these four shapes? How can you be sure?

_____

NOW TRY THIS!

● Draw seven 4 × 6 rectangles on squared paper.

● Which of the fractions below can be shown by shading only whole squares?

● Shade those areas that are possible and label them.

$\frac{3}{4}$ $\frac{5}{8}$ $\frac{1}{6}$ $\frac{7}{9}$ $\frac{7}{12}$ $\frac{5}{10}$ $\frac{3}{9}$

 Watch out for the last two fractions in the 'Now try this!' challenge – they are not given in their simplest forms.

Fractions made simple

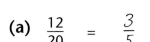

A Use **cancelling** to give these fractions in their simplest form.

$\dfrac{12}{20} = \dfrac{6}{10} = \dfrac{3}{5}$

(a) $\dfrac{12}{20} = \dfrac{3}{5}$

(b) $\dfrac{30}{52} = $ _____

(c) $\dfrac{16}{42} = $ _____

(d) $\dfrac{36}{90} = $ _____

(e) $\dfrac{40}{65} = $ _____

(f) $\dfrac{34}{51} = $ _____

(g) $\dfrac{42}{126} = $ _____

(h) $\dfrac{64}{120} = $ _____

(i) $\dfrac{80}{116} = $ _____

(j) $\dfrac{120}{180} = $ _____

(k) $\dfrac{144}{192} = $ _____

(l) $\dfrac{224}{264} = $ _____

B

1. In this survey, people were asked which one country they would like to visit this year.

> You need to find the total number of people. **!**

What fraction of the people surveyed would choose to visit:

Survey results	
Greece	8
Spain	9
France	12
USA	4
Portugal	3
Total	

(a) Greece? _____

(b) Spain? _____

(c) France? _____

(d) USA? _____

(e) Portugal? _____

2. In this survey, teenagers were asked to name the main activity they did last night.

What fraction of the teenagers said:

Survey results	
Computer games	8
Watching TV	7
Football practice	20
Dancing lessons	4
Horse riding	9
Total	

(a) computer games? _____

(b) watching TV? _____

(c) football practice? _____

(d) dancing lessons? _____

(e) horse riding? _____

Cancelling is where you divide a numerator and a denominator by the same number. Remember to give your answers as fractions in their simplest form. To do this, divide the **numerator** (top number) and the **denominator** (bottom number) by the same number until there is no other number that will divide exactly into both: for example $\frac{8}{20} = \frac{4}{10} = \frac{2}{5}$.

Developing Numeracy
Numbers and the Number System
Year 8
© A & C BLACK

Fractions made simple

C Read this football report.

Yesterday afternoon saw the long-awaited clash between United and City, and what a clash it was. **66 436** people, including **8696** children, saw City dominate the opening period. The **3256** City fans cheered their team's attacking play.

Their first shot on target came in the **6th** minute, they hit the bar in the **15th** and then had a penalty appeal turned down in the **35th** before scoring in the **44th**. United were on the back foot and did not manage a single shot until the **27th** minute.

All was to change, however, in the second half. United came out recharged and, when City had a man sent off in the **64th** minute, United took full advantage. They scored in the **66th** and **72nd** minutes to earn a **2–1** victory.

Match facts	City	United
Possession of the ball (min.)	54	36
Fouls	21	24
Offside offences	8	6

Answer the questions, giving your answers as fractions in their simplest form.

1. After what fraction of the 90-minute match did **City**:

(a) have their first shot? _____ (b) hit the bar? _____ (c) score? _____

(d) have a penalty appeal turned down? _____ (e) have a man sent off? _____

2. After what fraction of the 90-minute match did **United**:

(a) have their first shot? _____ (b) score their first goal? _____

(c) score their second goal? _____

3. What fraction of:

(a) the possession did each team have? City _____ United _____

(b) the fouls did each team commit? City _____ United _____

(c) the offside offences did each team commit? City _____ United _____

NOW TRY THIS!

● Use these digits to make at least six fractions equivalent to $\frac{5}{9}$. You can use the same digit more than once.

Example: $\frac{25}{45}$

To change a fraction to its simplest form, divide the **numerator** (top number) and the **denominator** (bottom number) by the same number until there is no other number that will divide exactly into both: for example $\frac{8}{20} = \frac{4}{10} = \frac{2}{5}$.

Developing Numeracy
Numbers and the Number System
Year 8
© A & C BLACK

33

Clever conversions

A

1. Convert each decimal to a fraction in its **simplest form**.

(a) 0.28 = $\frac{28}{100} = \frac{14}{50} = \frac{7}{25}$

(b) 0.32 =

(c) 0.48 =

(d) 0.64 =

(e) 0.72 =

(f) 0.84 =

(g) 0.96 =

(h) 0.125 = $\frac{125}{1000} = \frac{5}{40} = \frac{1}{8}$

(i) 0.275 =

(j) 0.375 =

(k) 0.448 =

(l) 0.625 =

(m) 0.875 =

(n) 0.928 =

2. (a) List the fractions which have a denominator of 8. _____

(b) What do you notice about their equivalent decimals? _____

_____

B

Join each decimal to its equivalent fractions.

0.375

0.125

0.475

0.625

0.64

0.875

$\frac{1}{8}$

$\frac{27}{72}$

$\frac{192}{300}$

$\frac{20}{32}$

$\frac{19}{40}$

$\frac{5}{8}$

$\frac{16}{25}$

$\frac{7}{8}$

$\frac{38}{80}$

$\frac{9}{24}$

$\frac{12}{96}$

$\frac{56}{64}$

$\frac{60}{96}$

$\frac{32}{50}$

$\frac{76}{160}$

$\frac{3}{8}$

To write a decimal as a fraction, remember that the column headings
for the digits to the right of the decimal point are tenths, hundredths,
thousandths, and so on. For a number with **one decimal place** the fraction
will have the denominator (bottom number) 10, for **two decimal places**
the denominator will be 100 and for **three decimal places** it will be 1000.

Developing Numeracy
Numbers and the Number System
Year 8
© A & C BLACK

Clever conversions

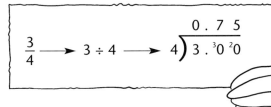

When you convert a fraction to a decimal, divide the numerator by the denominator, like this:

$$\frac{3}{4} \longrightarrow 3 \div 4 \longrightarrow 4\overline{)3\,.\,{}^{3}0\,{}^{2}0}^{0\,.\,7\,5}$$

Use this method to convert these fractions to decimals.

(a) $\frac{1}{4}$ =

(b) $\frac{1}{5}$ =

(c) $\frac{2}{5}$ =

(d) $\frac{1}{8}$ =

(e) $\frac{3}{5}$ =

(f) $\frac{3}{8}$ =

(g) $\frac{5}{8}$ =

(h) $\frac{4}{5}$ =

(i) $\frac{6}{8}$ =

(j) $\frac{7}{8}$ =

NOW TRY THIS!

● Use the same method to convert these fractions to decimals.

$$\frac{1}{9} \qquad \frac{1}{3} \qquad \frac{4}{9} \qquad \frac{1}{6} \qquad \frac{5}{9} \qquad \frac{2}{3} \qquad \frac{7}{9} \qquad \frac{5}{6}$$

● What do you notice? _____

A **proper fraction** is a fraction in which the denominator (bottom number) is larger than the numerator (top number). Proper fractions are always less than 1, so the equivalent decimal will begin with 0, for example $\frac{3}{4}$ = 0.75.

Relate fractions to division and convert with a calculator

Conversion patterns

A

1. Complete the table. Write the division answers as | proper fractions | and | mixed numbers |.

÷	2	3	4	5	6	7	8	9
1	$\frac{1}{2}$		$\frac{1}{4}$					
2	1							
3	$1\frac{1}{2}$							
4								
5								
6								
7								
8								
9								

2. Look down the columns of the table. What patterns do you notice?

_____

_____

B

1. Use the table above to convert these | improper fractions | to mixed numbers.

Remember: $\frac{7}{4}$ is equivalent to 7 ÷ 4.

(a) $\frac{7}{4}$ = _____   **(b)** $\frac{9}{7}$ = _____   **(c)** $\frac{8}{3}$ = _____

(d) $\frac{9}{5}$ = _____   **(e)** $\frac{8}{6}$ = _____   **(f)** $\frac{7}{2}$ = _____

(g) $\frac{7}{3}$ = _____   **(h)** $\frac{9}{4}$ = _____   **(i)** $\frac{8}{5}$ = _____

2. Now convert these improper fractions to decimals.

(a) $\frac{7}{4}$ = _____   **(b)** $\frac{9}{7}$ = _____   **(c)** $\frac{8}{3}$ = _____

(d) $\frac{9}{5}$ = _____   **(e)** $\frac{8}{6}$ = _____   **(f)** $\frac{7}{2}$ = _____

(g) $\frac{7}{3}$ = _____   **(h)** $\frac{9}{4}$ = _____   **(i)** $\frac{8}{5}$ = _____

A **proper fraction** has a denominator (bottom number) which is larger than the numerator (top number). An **improper fraction** has a numerator which is larger than the denominator. A **mixed number** has a whole number part and a fraction part.

Developing Numeracy
Numbers and the Number System
Year 8
© A & C BLACK

36

Conversion patterns

C

1. Complete this table. Write the division answers as decimals.

A dot above the digits shows recurring decimals. $0.1\dot{6}$ means the digit 6 repeats. $0.\dot{1}\dot{6}$ means 1 **and** 6 repeat.

0.16

÷	2	3	4	5	6	7	8	9
1	0.5	$0.\dot{3}$	0.25					
2	1							
3	1.5							
4								
5								
6								
7								
8								
9								

2. Use the table above to help you write these decimals as fractions.

(a) 0.3333333 = _____

(b) 0.375 = _____

(c) 0.625 = _____

(d) $0.1\dot{6}$ = _____

(e) 3.5 = _____

(f) 1.8 = _____

(g) $2.\dot{6}$ = _____

(h) $0.\dot{8}$ = _____

(i) $0.8\dot{3}$ = _____

(j) $0.\dot{1}4285\dot{7}$ = _____

(k) $1.\dot{3}$ = _____

(l) 0.875 = _____

NOW TRY THIS!

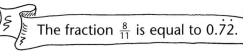

The fraction $\frac{8}{11}$ is equal to $0.\dot{7}\dot{2}$.

● Write fractions that are equal to these decimals. Use the fact on the banner to help you.

(a) $1.\dot{7}\dot{2}$ = _____

(b) $7.\dot{2}\dot{7}$ = _____

(c) $0.0\dot{7}\dot{2}$ = _____

(d) $0.\dot{3}\dot{6}$ = _____

(e) $1.\dot{3}\dot{6}$ = _____

(f) $0.\dot{1}\dot{8}$ = _____

For the 'Now try this!' challenge, think about how to increase a fraction by one whole, and how to make it ten times larger or smaller. You may use a calculator to test your ideas.

All in order?

A

This is Amy's method of ordering fractions.

$\frac{3}{4}$	$\frac{7}{10}$	$\frac{4}{5}$	$\frac{5}{8}$	$\frac{17}{20}$
$\frac{30}{40}$	$\frac{28}{40}$	$\frac{32}{40}$	$\frac{25}{40}$	$\frac{34}{40}$
3rd	2nd	4th	1st	5th

I change the fractions so that they all have the same denominator. Here all the denominators are factors of 40. Then I put them in ascending order!

Use Amy's method to put these fractions in **ascending order**.

(a)
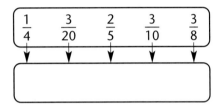

$\frac{1}{4}$ $\frac{3}{20}$ $\frac{2}{5}$ $\frac{3}{10}$ $\frac{3}{8}$

(b)
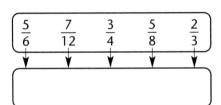

$\frac{5}{6}$ $\frac{7}{12}$ $\frac{3}{4}$ $\frac{5}{8}$ $\frac{2}{3}$

(c)
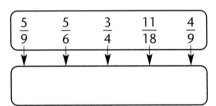

$\frac{5}{9}$ $\frac{5}{6}$ $\frac{3}{4}$ $\frac{11}{18}$ $\frac{4}{9}$

(d)
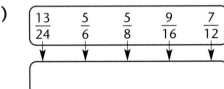

$\frac{13}{24}$ $\frac{5}{6}$ $\frac{5}{8}$ $\frac{9}{16}$ $\frac{7}{12}$

(e)
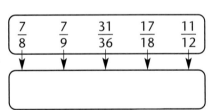

$\frac{7}{8}$ $\frac{7}{9}$ $\frac{31}{36}$ $\frac{17}{18}$ $\frac{11}{12}$

(f)
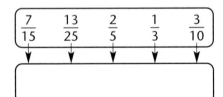

$\frac{7}{15}$ $\frac{13}{25}$ $\frac{2}{5}$ $\frac{1}{3}$ $\frac{3}{10}$

B

These fractions are meant to be arranged in ascending order, but there are mistakes.
Write the fractions correctly in ascending order.

(a) $\frac{17}{35}$ $\frac{1}{2}$ $\frac{3}{5}$ $\frac{37}{70}$ $\frac{4}{7}$

(b) $\frac{5}{6}$ $\frac{11}{21}$ $\frac{23}{42}$ $\frac{4}{7}$ $\frac{2}{3}$

(c) $\frac{5}{7}$ $\frac{42}{56}$ $\frac{25}{28}$ $\frac{11}{14}$ $\frac{7}{8}$

(d) $\frac{1}{6}$ $\frac{5}{18}$ $\frac{2}{9}$ $\frac{13}{54}$ $\frac{7}{27}$

To decide which number to use as the denominator of the equivalent fractions, find the **lowest common multiple** (LCM): for example, the LCM of 4, 6 and 8 is 24. This is because the numbers 4, 6 and 8 are all factors of 24, and 24 is the lowest number for which this is the case. **Ascending order** means in order from smallest to largest.

Developing Numeracy
Numbers and the Number System
Year 8
© A & C BLACK

All in order?

C

This is Luke's method of ordering fractions.

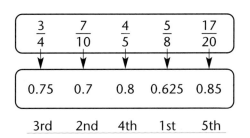

$\frac{3}{4}$	$\frac{7}{10}$	$\frac{4}{5}$	$\frac{5}{8}$	$\frac{17}{20}$
↓	↓	↓	↓	↓
0.75	0.7	0.8	0.625	0.85
3rd	2nd	4th	1st	5th

I change the fractions into decimals using a calculator. It's much easier to put decimals in ascending order!

1. Use Luke's method to put these fractions in **ascending order**.

(a)
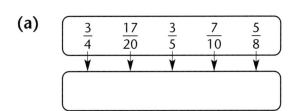

$\frac{3}{4}$	$\frac{17}{20}$	$\frac{3}{5}$	$\frac{7}{10}$	$\frac{5}{8}$

(b)

$\frac{8}{15}$	$\frac{12}{25}$	$\frac{3}{5}$	$\frac{2}{3}$	$\frac{7}{10}$

(c)
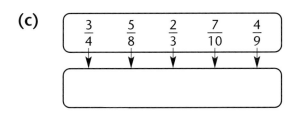

$\frac{3}{4}$	$\frac{5}{8}$	$\frac{2}{3}$	$\frac{7}{10}$	$\frac{4}{9}$

(d)
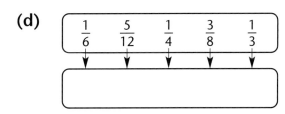

$\frac{1}{6}$	$\frac{5}{12}$	$\frac{1}{4}$	$\frac{3}{8}$	$\frac{1}{3}$

2. Here are Kate's test scores.

Maths (out of 47 marks)	36
Science (out of 38 marks)	29
English (out of 100 marks)	76
Geography (out of 25 marks)	18
History (out of 80 marks)	64

(a) In which subject did Kate score the highest proportion of marks?

(b) Write her scores as fractions in ascending order.

NOW TRY THIS!

- Use these ten numbers to make five **proper fractions**. Then write them in ascending order.

3	4	5	6	7	8	9	10	11	12

- Do this three more times. Make different fractions each time.

To order decimals, try writing them in columns, lining up the decimal points. Then compare the digits in each column, starting with the column furthest to the left. **Ascending order** means in order from smallest to largest. Remember that a **proper fraction** has a denominator (bottom number) which is larger than the numerator (top number).

Common knowledge

1. What is the **lowest common multiple** (LCM) of:

(a) 8 and 6? _24_   **(b)** 11 and 7? _____   **(c)** 10 and 8? _____

(d) 6 and 9? _____   **(e)** 5 and 15? _____   **(f)** 20 and 50? _____

(g) 3, 4 and 8? _____   **(h)** 4, 6 and 7? _____   **(i)** 4, 7 and 8? _____

2. Complete the equivalent fractions.

(a) $\frac{2}{3} = \frac{\quad}{24}$ **(b)** $\frac{3}{4} = \frac{\quad}{24}$ **(c)** $\frac{7}{8} = \frac{\quad}{24}$

(d) $\frac{7}{8} = \frac{\quad}{56}$ **(e)** $\frac{8}{9} = \frac{\quad}{27}$ **(f)** $\frac{4}{5} = \frac{\quad}{35}$

This flow diagram shows how you can add fractions with different denominators.

| S T A R T → | Look at the denominators and find the lowest common multiple (LCM). | → | Convert each fraction to an equivalent one with the LCM as its denominator. | → | Add the numerators to find the total. The denominator stays the same. | → | Change the improper fraction to a mixed number. | → | F I N I S H |

$\frac{2}{3} + \frac{3}{4} + \frac{7}{8}$ $\frac{?}{24} + \frac{?}{24} + \frac{?}{24}$ $\frac{16}{24} + \frac{18}{24} + \frac{21}{24} = \frac{55}{24}$ $\frac{55}{24} = 2\frac{7}{24}$

(LCM is 24)

3. Follow the flow diagram to find the total of each set of fractions.

(a) $\frac{3}{4} + \frac{6}{7} + \frac{5}{8} =$ _____

(b) $\frac{7}{9} + \frac{4}{5} + \frac{11}{15} =$ _____

(c) $\frac{3}{4} + \frac{1}{6} + \frac{8}{9} =$ _____

(d) $\frac{1}{4} + \frac{5}{6} + \frac{4}{7} =$ _____

Complete these subtractions using a similar method to part A.

(a) $\frac{7}{8} - \frac{4}{5} =$ _____   **(b)** $\frac{5}{6} - \frac{2}{5} =$ _____   **(c)** $\frac{3}{4} - \frac{1}{6} =$ _____

(d) $\frac{5}{6} - \frac{3}{8} =$ _____   **(e)** $\frac{6}{7} - \frac{3}{5} =$ _____   **(f)** $\frac{8}{9} - \frac{3}{5} =$ _____

 The **lowest common multiple** (LCM) is the lowest number into which all the numbers will divide without a remainder: for example, the LCM of 12 and 8 is 24.

Common knowledge

C

1. There is a mistake in each of these subtractions. Discuss them with a partner, then make the corrections.

(a) $\dfrac{7}{8} - \dfrac{3}{4} = \dfrac{28 - 24}{32} = \dfrac{4}{32} = \dfrac{1}{9}$

(b) $\dfrac{7}{8} - \dfrac{5}{6} = \dfrac{42 - 30}{24} = \dfrac{12}{24} = \dfrac{1}{2}$

(c) $\dfrac{5}{6} - \dfrac{2}{7} = \dfrac{35 - 12}{48} = \dfrac{23}{48}$

(d) $\dfrac{7}{9} - \dfrac{3}{4} = \dfrac{28 - 12}{36} = \dfrac{40}{36} = \dfrac{10}{9}$

2. Play this game with a partner.

$\dfrac{3}{8}$	$\dfrac{4}{5}$	$\dfrac{1}{6}$	$\dfrac{3}{4}$	$\dfrac{5}{7}$	$\dfrac{7}{8}$
$\dfrac{1}{10}$	$\dfrac{2}{3}$	$\dfrac{3}{7}$	$\dfrac{7}{10}$	$\dfrac{1}{5}$	$\dfrac{5}{6}$

☆ Take it in turns for one player to be 'Sum' and the other to be 'Difference'.
☆ Each player chooses a fraction from the grid above.
☆ The 'Sum' player finds the sum of the two fractions. The 'Difference' player finds the difference between them. Record both calculations.
☆ Score a point if your answer is one of the fractions below.
☆ The winner is the first player with five points.

$\dfrac{52}{60}$ $\dfrac{9}{56}$ $\dfrac{19}{30}$ $\dfrac{22}{35}$ $\dfrac{67}{40}$ $\dfrac{14}{24}$ $\dfrac{3}{10}$ $\dfrac{5}{21}$ $\dfrac{29}{20}$ $\dfrac{33}{28}$

Our calculations

NOW TRY THIS!

Unit fractions are fractions with a numerator of 1, like $\frac{1}{2}$ or $\frac{1}{4}$.

● Write these fractions as the sum of two unit fractions.

(a) $\dfrac{13}{40} = \dfrac{1}{8} + \dfrac{1}{5}$ (b) $\dfrac{5}{12} = $ _____ (c) $\dfrac{5}{6} = $ _____ (d) $\dfrac{5}{18} = $ _____

When adding or subtracting fractions, change the fractions to equivalent ones so that the denominators are all the same. Then all you need to do is add the numerators and change the answer to its simplest form.

Fraction file

1. Answer these questions.

(a) $\frac{5}{8}$ of 48 = $6 \times 5 = 30$ 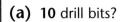 (b) $\frac{5}{6}$ of 36 = _____ (c) $\frac{5}{6}$ of 72 = _____

(d) $\frac{4}{9}$ of 108 = _____ 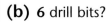 (e) $\frac{5}{7}$ of 91 = _____ (f) $\frac{7}{8}$ of 56 = _____

(g) $\frac{5}{9} \times 180$ = _____ (h) $\frac{7}{8} \times 160$ = _____ (i) $\frac{3}{4} \times 424$ = _____

2. A shop sells drill bits that are $\frac{3}{8}$ inch wide. If the drill bits are put side by side, what is the total width of:

(a) 10 drill bits? $\frac{3}{8} \times 10 = \frac{30}{8} = 3\frac{6}{8} = 3\frac{3}{4}$ $3\frac{3}{4}$ *inches*
(b) 6 drill bits?
(c) 9 drill bits?
(d) 22 drill bits?
(e) 25 drill bits?

3. The shop also sells drill bits that are $\frac{5}{8}$ inch wide. Answer questions **(a)** to **(e)** above for $\frac{5}{8}$ inch drill bits.

(a) _____ (b) _____ (c) _____

(d) _____ (e) _____

B Answer the questions on the wall. Write the answers as **mixed numbers**.

(a) $\frac{3}{4} \times 5 = 3\frac{3}{4}$ (b) $\frac{2}{3} \times 8 =$ (c) $\frac{2}{5} \times 7 =$ (d) $\frac{3}{4} \times 3 =$

(e) $\frac{7}{8} \times 12 =$ (f) $\frac{5}{6} \times 9 =$ (g) $\frac{3}{4} \times 11 =$

(h) $\frac{4}{7} \times 10 =$ (i) $\frac{3}{5} \times 6 =$ (j) $\frac{5}{9} \times 11 =$ (k) $\frac{7}{10} \times 3 =$

To find $\frac{4}{5}$ of 15, first find $\frac{1}{5}$ by dividing 15 by 5. Then multiply the answer by 4 to find $\frac{4}{5}$ ($3 \times 4 = 12$). Sometimes it is not easy to find $\frac{1}{5}$, for example when trying to find $\frac{4}{5}$ of 8. Here use a different method. Multiply the numerator by the whole number ($4 \times 8 = 32$). This means $\frac{32}{5}$. Now change this to a mixed number, giving the answer $6\frac{2}{5}$.

Developing Numeracy
Numbers and the Number System
Year 8
© A & C BLACK

Fraction file

C

$$\frac{5}{8} \times 28 \rightarrow \frac{5}{8} \times \frac{28}{1}$$

$$2\frac{5}{8} \times \frac{28^7}{1} = \frac{35}{2} = 17\frac{1}{2}$$

To multiply an integer by a fraction:
• make the integer into a fraction (over 1)
• try to cancel diagonally.
It makes the multiplying much easier!

1. Use the **cancelling** method above to answer these questions.

(a) $2\frac{5}{8} \times \frac{20^5}{1} = \frac{25}{2} = 12\frac{1}{2}$

(b) $\frac{5}{6} \times 21 =$ _____

(c) $\frac{4}{15} \times 45 =$ _____

(d) $\frac{3}{14} \times 35 =$ _____

(e) $\frac{7}{12} \times 18 =$ _____

(f) $\frac{5}{18} \times 36 =$ _____

(g) $35 \times \frac{6}{25} =$ _____

(h) $45 \times \frac{31}{60} =$ _____

2. Answer these questions. Use **cancelling** to help you.

(a) A block of cheese weighs 320 g. What is the mass of $\frac{5}{8}$ of the block?	**(b)** A block of cheese weighs 205 g. What is the mass of $\frac{3}{10}$ of the block?
(c) A block of cheese weighs 198 g. What is the mass of $\frac{7}{18}$ of the block?	**(d)** A block of cheese weighs 180 g. What is the mass of $\frac{5}{24}$ of the block?

NOW TRY THIS!

• Tick to show whether this statement is true or false.
• Write three examples to prove your answer.

Multiplying a positive number by a fraction less than one gives a smaller result.

True	
False	

 Cancelling is where you divide a numerator and a denominator by the same number. Remember that to multiply fractions, you multiply the numerators together and the denominators together.

Fraction division

A Drill bits come in different widths. A wooden box holds one layer of drill bits touching side by side. If the box is 15 inches wide, how many $\frac{1}{2}$ inch drill bits will it hold?

How many halves in 15?

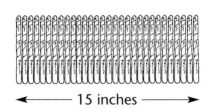

← 15 inches →

30!

1. How many of these drill bits fit into a **16 inch** box?

   (a) $\frac{1}{2}$ inch _32_   **(b)** $\frac{1}{4}$ inch _____

   (c) $\frac{1}{8}$ inch _____   **(d)** $\frac{1}{16}$ inch _____

2. How many of these drill bits fit into a **24 inch** box?

   (a) $\frac{1}{2}$ inch _____   **(b)** $\frac{1}{4}$ inch _____

   (c) $\frac{3}{4}$ inch _____   **(d)** $\frac{1}{8}$ inch _____

   (e) $\frac{3}{8}$ inch _____   **(f)** $\frac{1}{6}$ inch _____

3. How many of these drill bits fit into a **30 inch** box?

   (a) $\frac{1}{2}$ inch _____   **(b)** $\frac{1}{5}$ inch _____

   (c) $\frac{3}{5}$ inch _____   **(d)** $\frac{1}{6}$ inch _____

   (e) $\frac{5}{6}$ inch _____   **(f)** $\frac{2}{5}$ inch _____

B Rewrite the questions and answers above using the division sign.

   1. (a) _$16 \div \frac{1}{2} = 32$_   **2. (a)** _____   **3. (a)** _____

   (b) _____   **(b)** _____   **(b)** _____

   (c) _____   **(c)** _____   **(c)** _____

   (d) _____   **(d)** _____   **(d)** _____

   (e) _____   **(e)** _____

   (f) _____   **(f)** _____

   What do you notice about dividing a positive integer by a fraction?

   _____

 To divide an integer (a whole number) by a fraction, ask yourself: 'How many of this fraction are there in this number?' For example, for $12 \div \frac{1}{4}$ ask, 'How many quarters are there in 12?' There are 4 quarters in one whole so there must be 4×12 in 12 wholes, giving the answer 48.

Developing Numeracy
Numbers and the Number System
Year 8
© A & C BLACK

Fraction division

C Answer these division questions.

(a)
How many lots of one-fifth are there in the number 6?

$$6 \div \frac{1}{5} = 30$$

(b)
How many lots of two-fifths are there in the number 6?

(c)
How many lots of one-ninth are there in the number 15?

(d)
How many lots of three-ninths are there in the number 15?

(e)
What is 9 divided by $\frac{1}{8}$?

(f)
What is 9 divided by $\frac{3}{8}$?

(g)
What is 10 divided by $\frac{1}{6}$?

(h)
What is 10 divided by $\frac{5}{6}$?

(i)
$27 \div \frac{1}{10} = ?$

(j)
$27 \div \frac{9}{10} = ?$

NOW TRY THIS!

- Tick to show whether this statement is true or false.
- Write three examples to prove your answer.

Dividing a positive number by a fraction less than one gives a smaller result.

True	
False	

_____ _____ _____

To divide a whole number by a fraction, ask yourself: 'How many of this fraction are there in this number?' For example, for $12 \div \frac{1}{4}$ ask, 'How many quarters are there in 12?' There are 4 quarters in one whole so there must be 4 × 12 in 12 wholes, giving the answer 48.

Developing Numeracy
Numbers and the Number System
Year 8
© A & C BLACK

45

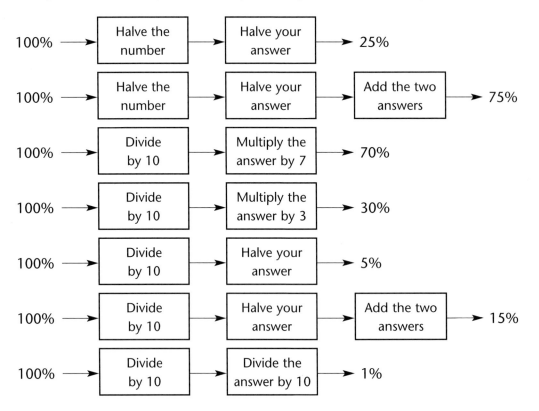

Many methods

A These diagrams show how you can find percentages of a number in your head.

100% → Halve the number → Halve your answer → 25%

100% → Halve the number → Halve your answer → Add the two answers → 75%

100% → Divide by 10 → Multiply the answer by 7 → 70%

100% → Divide by 10 → Multiply the answer by 3 → 30%

100% → Divide by 10 → Halve your answer → 5%

100% → Divide by 10 → Halve your answer → Add the two answers → 15%

100% → Divide by 10 → Divide the answer by 10 → 1%

Use the diagrams above to help you answer these questions mentally.

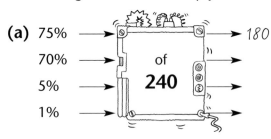

(a) 75% → *180*
70% →
5% →
1% →

of **240**

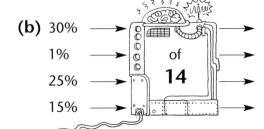

(b) 30% →
1% →
25% →
15% →

of **14**

B Read how Zoe answered this percentage question.

Find 7% of £48

First I worked out 1% of 48 by dividing it by 100 in my head.
Then I used a written method to multiply 1% by 7, like this:

I know that 1% of 48 is 0.48

$$\begin{array}{r} 0.48 \\ \times\ 7 \\ \hline 3.36 \end{array}$$

So 7% of £48 is **£3.36**

Use Zoe's method to answer these questions.

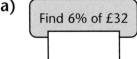
(a) Find 6% of £32

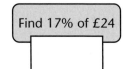
(b) Find 17% of £24

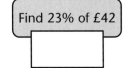
(c) Find 23% of £42

There are many different ways of calculating percentages. You can do it mentally, on paper or using a calculator. You may have other ways of working out the answers in your head or on paper.

**Developing Numeracy
Numbers and the Number System
Year 8**
© A & C BLACK

Many methods

 Calculate percentages mentally or using informal methods

1. Write these quiz scores as percentages.

> To write one number as a percentage of another, make a fraction and then change the fraction to a percentage. **!**

(a)

I scored 3 out of 10.

$$\frac{3}{10} = \frac{30}{100} = 30\%$$

(b)

I scored 42 out of 50.

(c)

I scored 13 out of 20.

(d)

I scored 18 out of 25.

(e)

I scored 4 out of 5.

(f)

I scored 275 out of 500.

2. Answer the percentage questions.

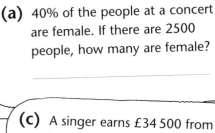

(a) 40% of the people at a concert are female. If there are 2500 people, how many are female?

(b) 75% of the pupils in Year 8 did not go to the concert. If there are 224 pupils in Year 8, how many did not go to the concert?

(c) A singer earns £34 500 from her latest single. She pays 6% of her income to her manager. How much does the manager earn?

(d) Jade earns £238. She spends 30% of this on concert tickets. How much does she spend?

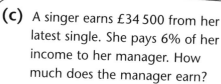

NOW TRY THIS!

- Write **£60** in the middle of a sheet of paper. Find at least 20 different percentages of this amount.

50% of £60 = £30

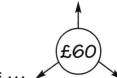

Example: 5% of £60 = ...   £60   1% of £60 = ...

 Make sure you write answers in pounds and pence instead of as ordinary decimals, for example 0.6 should be written as £0.60 or 60p.

Developing Numeracy
Numbers and the Number System
Year 8
© A & C BLACK

47

Calculator calculations

A Sam is explaining how she used a calculator to answer this question.

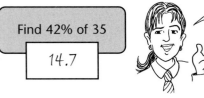

Find 42% of 35

14.7

First I found 1% of 35 by dividing 35 by 100 in my head: 35 ÷ 100 = 0.35.
Now that I knew 1%, I could find 42% by multiplying 0.35 by 42.
I got the answer **14.7**.

Use Sam's method to solve these problems.

(a) Find 56% of 35

(b) Find 27% of 14

(c) Find 42% of 31

(d) Find 53% of 64

(e) Find 74% of 69

(f) Find 73% of 16

(g) Find 89% of 89

(h) Find 94% of 94

(i) Find 99% of 99

B Ben is explaining how he used a calculator to answer this question.

Find 57% of £48

£27.36

I changed 57% to the decimal 0.57 in my head.
To find 57% of 48, I keyed in '0.57 × 48 ='
and got the answer 27.36.
So, 57% of £48 = **£27.36**.

Use Ben's method to solve these problems.

(a) Find 57% of £54

(b) Find 18% of £76

(c) Find 31% of £19

(d) Find 62% of £51

(e) Find 76% of £83

(f) Find 69% of £69

(g) Find 17.5% of £38

(h) Find 24.5% of £86

(i) Find 97.5% of £98

Remember that the percentage sign (%) means 'out of one hundred' or 'for every one hundred'. When you write answers as amounts of money, remember to write £23.40 not 23.4.

Developing Numeracy
Numbers and the Number System
Year 8
© A & C BLACK

48

Calculator calculations

C

1. Join pairs that show the same amount.

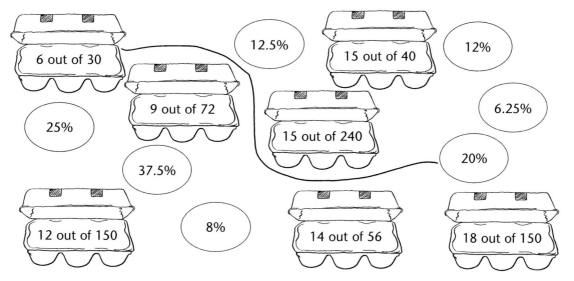

6 out of 30

12.5%

15 out of 40

12%

9 out of 72

25%

6.25%

15 out of 240

20%

37.5%

12 out of 150

8%

14 out of 56

18 out of 150

2. Solve these percentage problems.

(a) This pie chart shows how the matches in the football league finished one Saturday. There were 20 matches. How many home teams won their matches? _____

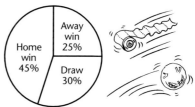

Home win 45% · Away win 25% · Draw 30%

(b) On average, Eggs'R'Us reject 9 out of every 400 eggs because of cracking. What is this as a percentage? _____

(c) £2300 was paid to the estate agents Doolittle, Allday and Knight. 17.5% of the money was VAT. How much was paid in VAT? _____

(d) On a mountain, the windspeed was recorded as gale force on 292 days out of 365 last year. What percentage is this? _____

(e) In a Pop Star competition, approximately 19 million people voted. Of this number, about 65.2% voted for the winner. How many people did *not* vote for the winner? _____

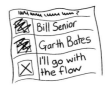

Bill Senior · Garth Bates · I'll go with the flow

NOW TRY THIS!

• Solve this puzzle.

> 80% of a class are girls. 75% of the girls and 25% of the boys have a packed lunch. What percentage of the class has a packed lunch? _____ %

• Make up three puzzles like this for a partner to solve.

To write a fraction as a percentage, remember that you can use your calculator to divide the **numerator** (top number) by the **denominator** (bottom number), and multiply the answer by one hundred: for example, to find the fraction $\frac{6}{30}$ as a percentage, key in 6 ÷ 30 × 100 = [20%].

Percentage problems

A

1. Find what **percentage** of each bag of bird food is crushed maize.

(a)

Morning Chorus

50% sunflower seeds

$\frac{1}{4}$ peanuts

10% wheat

_____ crushed maize

(b)

Dawn Mix

47% sunflower seeds

30% peanuts

$\frac{1}{10}$ wheat

_____ crushed maize

(c)

Soft-bill Mix

28% sunflower seeds

$\frac{1}{20}$ peanuts

28% wheat

_____ crushed maize

2. Do you get more sunflower seeds if you buy:

   (a) 300 g of Morning Chorus or 500 g of Soft-bill Mix? _____

   (b) 450 g of Morning Chorus or 500 g of Dawn Mix? _____

   (c) 650 g of Soft-bill Mix or 350 g of Dawn Mix? _____

3. Do you get more peanuts if you buy:

   (a) 400 g of Morning Chorus or 300 g of Dawn Mix? _____

   (b) 100 g of Morning Chorus or 800 g of Soft-bill Mix? _____

4. Do you get more wheat if you buy:

   (a) 750 g of Dawn Mix or 450 g of Soft-bill Mix? _____

   (b) 800 g of Morning Chorus or 500 g of Soft-bill Mix? _____

B Write the fraction (F), decimal (D) and percentage (P) equivalents to complete these tables. Write fractions in their simplest form.

1.

	F	D	P
(a)	$\frac{1}{10}$		
(b)	$\frac{3}{4}$		
(c)	$\frac{27}{100}$		

2.

	F	D	P
(a)		0.01	
(b)		0.4	
(c)		0.81	

3.

	F	D	P
(a)			32%
(b)			8%
(c)			37.5%

To change a fraction to its simplest form, divide the **numerator** (top number) and the **denominator** (bottom number) by the same number until there is no other number that will divide exactly into both: for example, for $\frac{8}{10}$ both numbers can be divided by the whole number 2 so this fraction is written as $\frac{4}{5}$ in its simplest form.

**Developing Numeracy
Numbers and the Number System
Year 8**
© A & C BLACK

Percentage problems

C Use this table to help you answer the questions below.

Find out how much metal is needed for one coin first. **!**

BANK

Coin	Composite (approximate)	Mass
1 Eurocent	94% steel, 6% copper	2.3 g
2 Eurocent	94.5% steel, 5.5% copper	3.06 g
5 Eurocent	95% steel, 5% copper	3.92 g
10 Eurocent	89% copper, 5% aluminium, 5% zinc, 1% tin	4.1 g
20 Eurocent	89% copper, 5% aluminium, 5% zinc, 1% tin	5.74 g
50 Eurocent	89% copper, 5% aluminium, 5% zinc, 1% tin	7.8 g
1 Euro	Inner: 75% copper, 25% nickel Outer: 75% copper, 20% zinc, 5% nickel	(Inner 3.71 g) (Outer 3.79 g) **Total** 7.5 g
2 Euro	Inner: 75% copper, 20% zinc, 5% nickel Outer: 75% copper, 25% nickel	(Inner 4.1 g) (Outer 4.4 g) **Total** 8.5 g

1. How many grams of **copper** are needed to make:

   (a) ten 5 Eurocent coins? _1.96 g_

   (b) one hundred 20 Eurocent coins? _____

   (c) one thousand 2 Eurocent coins? _____

   (d) ten thousand 1 Euro coins? _____

   (e) ten thousand 2 Euro coins? _____

2. When making one hundred thousand 50 Eurocent coins, how much:

   (a) copper is needed? _____

   (b) zinc is needed? _____

   (c) aluminium is needed? _____

   (d) tin is needed? _____

NOW TRY THIS!

● ▦ If you wanted to make one of each of the coins listed above, how many grams of each metal would you need?

   (a) copper   **(b)** zinc   **(c)** steel

   (d) aluminium   **(e)** tin   **(f)** nickel

 Watch out for the compositions of the 1 and 2 Euro coins. They have an inner and outer section, so calculate each part separately.

Percentage increases

A

1. Follow the trail and find these percentages.

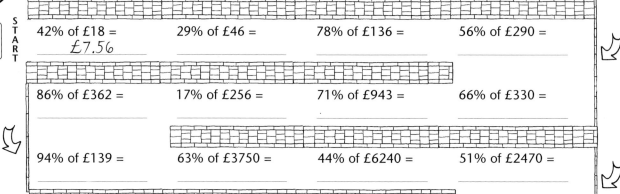

START

| 42% of £18 = £7.56 | 29% of £46 = | 78% of £136 = | 56% of £290 = |

| 86% of £362 = | 17% of £256 = | 71% of £943 = | 66% of £330 = |

| 94% of £139 = | 63% of £3750 = | 44% of £6240 = | 51% of £2470 = |

FINISH

| 87% of £32 700 = | 99% of £6200 = | 38% of £2995 = | 73% of £2740 = |

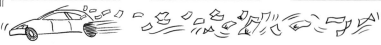

This flow diagram shows you how to **increase** an amount by a percentage.

START →
| Find the percentage of the original amount. | → | Increase the original amount by adding your answer to it. | → | This gives you the new amount. |
→ FINISH

Example:
Increase £160 by 15%   15% of £160 = £24   £160 + £24 =   £184

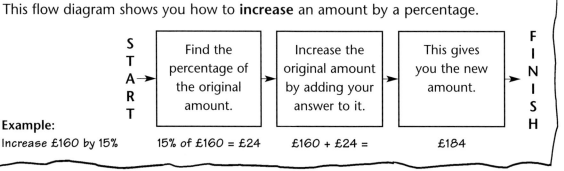

2. (a) Increase £120 by 45%. _____

(b) Increase £450 by 24%. _____

(c) Increase £1250 by 95%. _____

B

Complete this percentage increase table.

Original amount	Percentage increase	Amount to be increased by	New amount	New amount as percentage of old amount
£45	15%	£6.75	£51.75	115%
£85	28%			128%
£136	64%			
£260	46%			
£1126	29%			

 One way to find a percentage of an amount is to think of the percentage as a decimal and multiply this decimal by the given amount: for example, 42% of £18 equals 0.42 × £18 = £7.56. In part B, the new amount will always be more than 100% because the original amount is being increased.

Developing Numeracy
Numbers and the Number System
Year 8
© A & C BLACK

Percentage increases

C How quickly can you answer these questions? Time yourself.

(a) The number of employees increased by 28% in one year. At the beginning of the year there were 250 employees. How many were there at the end of the year?

(b) A footballer earned £43 000 per week. He was given a 4% rise. How much does he earn per week now?

(c) A car was travelling at 40 mph. The car's speed increased by 16%. What speed is the car now travelling at?

(d) A baby's mass was 3000 g. It increased by 12%. What is the baby's new mass?

(e) I paid £300 into my savings account. At the end of the year this amount was increased by 6%. How much money do I have now?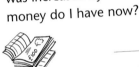

(f) The population of Whitlake increased by 34% in 2002. At the beginning of the year there were 72 800 people. How many were there at the end of the year?

 Whitlake pop 72800 going up!

(g) The attendance at a football ground increased by 48% over one season. At the beginning of the season the attendance was 36 100. What was it at the end of the season?

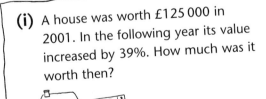

(h) A shop made 17% more money on Tuesday than on Monday. On Monday it made £965. How much did it make on Tuesday?

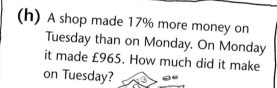

(i) A house was worth £125 000 in 2001. In the following year its value increased by 39%. How much was it worth then?

(j) A shop has increased its prices by 13%. How much does a coat cost if its original price was £37?

NOW TRY THIS!

 • The value of a house increased by 25%.

Its **new** value is £45 200. What was the **original** value? _____

 To help you with the 'Now try this!' challenge, think about how many per cent the new value is. Use this to find what 1% is worth and then to find what 100% (the original amount) is worth.

Developing Numeracy
Numbers and the Number System
Year 8
© A & C BLACK

Percentage decreases

A

This flow diagram shows you how to **decrease** an amount by a percentage.

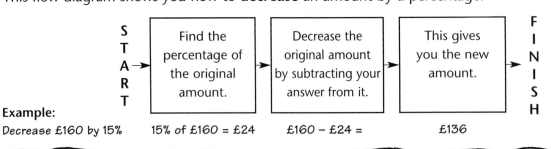

| S T A R T | → | Find the percentage of the original amount. | → | Decrease the original amount by subtracting your answer from it. | → | This gives you the new amount. | → | F I N I S H |

Example:

Decrease £160 by 15%   15% of £160 = £24   £160 − £24 =   £136

1. **(a)** Decrease £120 by 45%. _____

   (b) Decrease £450 by 24%. _____

   (c) Decrease £1250 by 95%. _____

   (d) Decrease £4560 by 88%. _____

2. Complete this percentage decrease table.

Original amount	Percentage decrease	Amount to be decreased by	New amount	New amount as percentage of old amount
£45	15%	£6.75	£38.25	85%
£85	28%			72%
£136	64%			
£260	46%			
£842	13%			
£1126	29%			

B

Solve these percentage decrease problems.

(a) The value of a car decreased by 47% in one year. At the beginning of the year its value was £2750. What was its value at the end of the year?

(b) A car was travelling at 40 mph. The car's speed decreased by 15%. What speed is the car now travelling at?

(c) The population of a village was 360 people. It decreased by 35%. What is the village's population now?

(d) A person's mass was 54 kg. It decreased by 12%. What is the person's new mass?

One way to find a percentage of an amount is to think of the percentage as a decimal and multiply this decimal by the given amount: for example, 15% of 45 equals 0.15 × 45 = 6.75.

Percentage decreases

Play this game with a partner. You each need a dice and a counter.

- ☆ Each player starts with £100 holiday money.
- ☆ Take turns to roll the dice and move your counter around the trail.
- ☆ Use your calculator to increase or decrease your sum of money by the amount shown.
- ☆ Round your answers to two decimal places. Keep a record of your running total.
- ☆ Go round the trail three times. The winner is the player with the most money at the end.

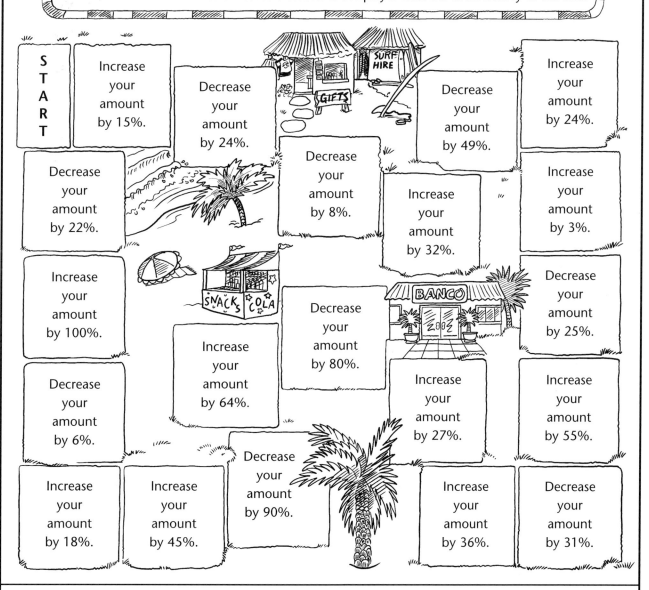

START

Increase your amount by 15%.

Decrease your amount by 24%.

Decrease your amount by 49%.

Increase your amount by 24%.

Decrease your amount by 22%.

Decrease your amount by 8%.

Increase your amount by 32%.

Increase your amount by 3%.

Increase your amount by 100%.

Decrease your amount by 25%.

Decrease your amount by 6%.

Increase your amount by 64%.

Decrease your amount by 80%.

Increase your amount by 27%.

Increase your amount by 55%.

Increase your amount by 18%.

Increase your amount by 45%.

Decrease your amount by 90%.

Increase your amount by 36%.

Decrease your amount by 31%.

NOW TRY THIS!

- Explain in words (*without* using the word 'percentage') what will happen to an amount if you:

(a) increase it by 100%

(b) decrease it by 49%

(c) increase it by 90%

(d) decrease it by 100%

One way to find a percentage of an amount is to think of the percentage as a decimal and multiply this decimal by the given amount: for example, 45% of 36 equals 0.45 × 36 = 16.2. To decrease the original amount by this percentage, subtract the answer from the original amount.

Solve problems involving ratio and proportion, and simplest form

Do the splits

 A Change these ratios to their simplest form.

(a)
$$\begin{array}{ccc} A & : & B & : & C \\ 15 & : & 18 & : & 21 \\ \downarrow & & \downarrow & & \downarrow \\ 5 & : & 6 & : & 7 \end{array}$$

(b)
$$\begin{array}{ccc} A & : & B & : & C \\ 12 & : & 18 & : & 30 \\ \downarrow & & \downarrow & & \downarrow \\ \_ & : & \_ & : & \_ \end{array}$$

(c)
$$\begin{array}{ccc} A & : & B & : & C \\ 14 & : & 28 & : & 21 \\ \downarrow & & \downarrow & & \downarrow \\ \_ & : & \_ & : & \_ \end{array}$$

(d) 36 : 18 : 6
_ : _ : _

(e) 25 : 75 : 90
_ : _ : _

(f) 32 : 64 : 16
_ : _ : _

(g) 200 : 150 : 300
_ : _ : _

(h) 450 : 150 : 300
_ : _ : _

(i) 125 : 175 : 200
_ : _ : _

(j) 124 : 136 : 100
_ : _ : _

(k) 112 : 640 : 320
_ : _ : _

(l) 88 : 121 : 110
_ : _ : _

B For each of the ratios **(a)** to **(i)** above, write the ⎡proportion⎤ of the total number of parts for A, B and C. Write the proportions as fractions in their simplest form.

(a)
$$\begin{array}{ccc} A & : & B & : & C \\ 5 & : & 6 & : & 7 \end{array}$$
$A = \dfrac{5}{18}$ $B = \dfrac{1}{3}$ $C = \dfrac{7}{18}$

(b) _____   A = ____   B = ____   C = ____

(c) _____   A = ____   B = ____   C = ____

(d) _____   A = ____   B = ____   C = ____

(e) _____   A = ____   B = ____   C = ____

(f) _____   A = ____   B = ____   C = ____

(g) _____   A = ____   B = ____   C = ____

(h) _____   A = ____   B = ____   C = ____

(i) _____   A = ____   B = ____   C = ____

 To change ratios to their simplest form, find a number that is a factor of all the numbers in the ratio, and divide each number in the ratio by this factor. When you can no longer do this, the ratio is in its simplest form. **Proportion** compares one part with the whole, for example the number of parts for A out of the total number of parts (A + B + C).

Developing Numeracy
Numbers and the Number System
Year 8
© A & C BLACK

Do the splits

C Mira is explaining how to answer this ratio question.

Divide £56 in the ratio of 1 : 2 : 5

Find how many parts are in the ratio:
1 + 2 + 5 = 8 parts.
Then find what one part is worth by dividing the amount by the number of parts:
£56 ÷ 8 = £7, so one part is worth £7.
Finally, multiply to get the answer: £7, £14, £35.

Use this method to answer the questions.

(a) Ann, Brian and Robin split £68 in the ratio 4 : 6 : 7. How much does each person get? _____

(b) Three angles meet at a point (so they have a total of 360°) and are in the ratio 2 : 3 : 5. What are their sizes? _____

(c) In a recipe, Claire uses 3 parts flour to 2 parts sugar to 4 parts butter. If she makes 684 g of this mix, how much of each ingredient will she need? _____

If you are told what one person's share is, use the number of parts **they** have, to find what one part is worth.

(d) Ann, Brian and Robin split some money in the ratio 4 : 6 : 7. If Ann gets £24, how much do the others get? _____

(e) Three angles are in the ratio 2 : 3 : 5. The largest angle is 75°. What are the other two angles? _____

(f) In a recipe, Claire uses 3 parts flour to 2 parts sugar to 4 parts butter. If she uses 88 g of butter, how much of the other ingredients will she need?

_____

NOW TRY THIS!

This is the scale of a map.   1 cm : 200 m

● What distances on the ground do these lengths on the map represent?

  (a) 4 cm _____   **(b)** 22 cm _____   **(c)** 48 cm _____

● What lengths on the map will represent these distances on the ground?

  (d) 100 m _____   **(e)** 2 km _____   **(f)** 3.2 km _____

 You can multiply or divide the numbers in a ratio by any number, and so long as you do the same to **all** the numbers, the relationship will still be the same.

Get things in proportion

A Complete these proportion charts.

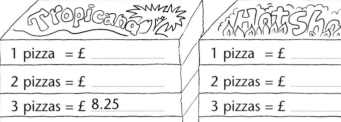

(a)

1 pizza = £ _____
2 pizzas = £ _____
3 pizzas = £ 8.25
4 pizzas = £ _____
5 pizzas = £ _____
6 pizzas = £ _____

(b)

1 pizza = £ _____
2 pizzas = £ _____
3 pizzas = £ _____
4 pizzas = £ _____
5 pizzas = £ 15.25
6 pizzas = £ _____

(c)

1 pizza = £ _____
2 pizzas = £ _____
3 pizzas = £ _____
4 pizzas = £ 19.92
5 pizzas = £ _____
6 pizzas = £ _____

As the number of pizzas increases, so does the price. We say these are in ⬛ direct proportion ⬛.

B These signs show the relationship between miles and kilometres.

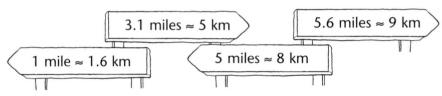

3.1 miles ≈ 5 km

5.6 miles ≈ 9 km

1 mile ≈ 1.6 km

5 miles ≈ 8 km

1. Plot the distances on the conversion chart and join them with a straight line.

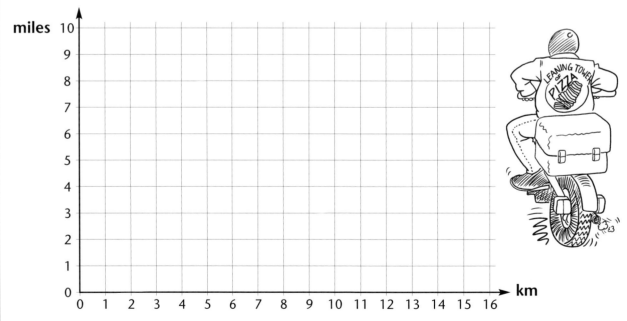

miles

2. Use the chart to estimate equivalent measurements for these distances.

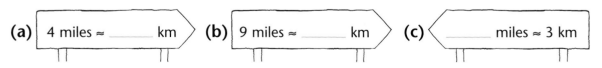

(a) 4 miles ≈ _____ km   **(b)** 9 miles ≈ _____ km   **(c)** _____ miles ≈ 3 km

Things are in **direct proportion** when, as one thing increases, so does the other: for example, as the number of miles increases, so does the number of kilometres.

Developing Numeracy
Numbers and the Number System
Year 8
© A & C BLACK

Get things in proportion

C

Jake has rushed his homework and has made mistakes. Mark his work with a tick or a cross and make corrections for him.

You'll need to find what one unit is worth first.

!

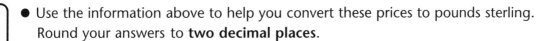

Homework

(a) If £2 is worth 2.92 US dollars, how many US dollars will I get for £38?
US $55.48

(b) If £5 is worth 916.9 Japanese yen, how many yen will I get for £23?
199.33 yen

(c) If £7 is worth 79.52 Hong Kong dollars, how many HK dollars will I get for £48?
HK $545.28

(d) If £11 is worth 17.38 euros, how many euros will I get for £48?
€75.84

(e) If £8 is worth 39.28 Argentine pesos, how many pesos will I get for £48?
0.1 pesos

(f) If £15 is worth 100.65 Egypt pounds, how many Egypt pounds will I get for £36?
3623.40 Egypt pounds

(g) If £32 is worth 4258.56 Iceland kronur, how many kronur will I get for £75?
57.55 kronur

(h) If £48 is worth 3420.48 Indian rupees, how many rupees will I get for £128?
437821.44 rupees

NOW TRY THIS!

● Use the information above to help you convert these prices to pounds sterling. Round your answers to **two decimal places**.

(a) 22.63 US dollars   = £ _____   **(b)** 3869.32 yen   = £ _____

(c) 161.31 HK dollars = £ _____   **(d)** 56.4 euros   = £ _____

(e) 374 Argentine pesos = £ _____   **(f)** 202 Egypt pounds   = £ _____

(g) 856 Iceland kronur = £ _____   **(h)** 57 863.12 Indian rupees = £ _____

Find out what one pound is worth first and use this to help you answer the questions. For example, if £2 is worth 2.92 US dollars, £1 is worth 2.92 ÷ 2 = 1.46 US dollars. So £38 is worth 1.46 × 38 = 55.48 US dollars.

Answers

p 8

A1
(a) 100   one hundred
(b) 1000   one thousand
(c) 10 000   ten thousand
(d) 100 000   one hundred thousand
(e) 1 000 000   one million
(f) 10 000 000   ten million
(g) 100 000 000   one hundred million
(h) 1 000 000 000   one billion

A2
(a) 10×10
(b) $10 \times 10 \times 10$
(c) $10 \times 10 \times 10 \times 10$
(d) $10 \times 10 \times 10 \times 10 \times 10$
The number of zeros = the number of tens in the answer.

B
(a) $100 = 10 \times 10 = 10^2$
(b) $1000 = 10 \times 10 \times 10 = 10^3$
(c) $10\,000 = 10 \times 10 \times 10 \times 10 = 10^4$
(d) $100\,000 = 10 \times 10 \times 10 \times 10 \times 10 = 10^5$
(e) $1\,000\,000 = 10 \times 10 \times 10 \times 10 \times 10 \times 10 = 10^6$
(f) $10\,000\,000 = 10 \times 10 \times 10 \times 10 \times 10 \times 10 \times 10 = 10^7$
(g) $100\,000\,000 =$
$\quad 10 \times 10 \times 10 \times 10 \times 10 \times 10 \times 10 \times 10 = 10^8$
(h) $1\,000\,000\,000 =$
$\quad 10 \times 10 \times 10 \times 10 \times 10 \times 10 \times 10 \times 10 \times 10 = 10^9$

p 9

C1
(a) 3 000 000   (b) 5 000 000
(c) 800 000   (d) 90 000 000
(e) 1 500 000   (f) 3400
(g) 82 000

C2
(a) 700 000 000   (b) 70 000 000
(c) 1 800 000 000   (d) 420 000 000

p 10

A1
(a) 0.6   (b) 0.7   (c) 1.5
(d) 2   (e) 5   (f) 9.2

A2
(a) 0.6   (b) 0.7   (c) 1.5
(d) 2   (e) 5   (f) 9.2

A3 They give the same answer.

A4 (a) 0.06   (b) 0.07   (c) 0.15

A5 (a) 0.06   (b) 0.07   (c) 0.15

A6 They give the same answer.

A7 Multiplying by 10.

A8 Multiplying by 100.

B
(a) 6   (b) 0.27   (c) 630   (d) 800
(e) 3.4   (f) 0.45   (g) 510   (h) 7300

p 11

C1
(a) T   (b) F   (c) T
(d) T   (e) F   (f) T

C2 Both trails give a finish number that is 100 times greater than the start number.

p 12

A1 Numbers correctly filled in on number lines. Pupils can be asked to use a calculator to check these if necessary.

A2
(a) <   (b) <   (c) >
(d) >   (e) >   (f) >
(g) >   (h) <   (i) <

B
(a) 5.088 km   5.8 km   5.801 km   5.81 km
(b) 6.67 l   6.676 l   6.7 l   6.776 l
(c) 0.059 m   0.53 m   0.531 m   0.54 m
(d) 1.889 kg   1.89 kg   1.892 kg   1.9 kg

p 13

C1
(a) Turgenev
(b) Gambettan

C2 Turgenev and Millbrook

C3
(a) 10 kg, 4.999 kg, 1.7 kg, 0.68 kg, 0.14 kg, 0.1 kg, 0.056 kg, 0.039 kg, 0.03 kg, 0.012 kg
(b) dolphin, elephant, whale (1.7 kg, 4.999 kg, 10 kg)
(c) baboon 0.14 kg, kangaroo 0.056 kg, racoon 0.039 kg, monkey 0.1 kg, cat 0.03 kg, rabbit 0.012 kg
(d) 0.002 kg

p 14

A1

£628 060	£628 100	£628 000	£630 000
£512 780	£512 800	£513 000	£510 000
£405 450	£405 500	£405 000	£410 000
£816 720	£816 700	£817 000	£820 000
£554 520	£554 500	£555 000	£550 000
£813 890	£813 900	£814 000	£810 000
£161 980	£162 000	£162 000	£160 000
£759 920	£759 900	£760 000	£760 000
£199 900	£199 900	£200 000	£200 000
£248 000	£248 000	£248 000	£250 000
£750 000	£750 000	£750 000	£750 000
£500 000	£500 000	£500 000	£500 000

A2 The man has rounded the number to the nearest million. The woman has rounded to the nearest hundred thousand.

B Between the given ranges

784 075 → 784 084	780 000	
469 565 → 469 574	470 000	
986 545 → 986 549	986 600	990 000
109 500 → 109 549		
109 450 → 109 499		
149 995 → 150 004		

p 15

C
(a) 33 500   (b) 19 500   (c) 22 650   (d) 55 850
    34 499   20 499   22 749   55 949
(e) 15 000   (f) 75 000   (g) 66 950   (h) 9995
    24 999   84 999   67 049   10 004

Now try this!
Lowest 45 000   Highest 45 499

p 16

A

47.3125	47	47.3	47.31
34.1875	34	34.2	34.19
286.4375	286	286.4	286.44
343.0625	343	343.1	343.06
446.8125	447	446.8	446.81
528.1875	528	528.2	528.19
493.625	494	493.6	493.63
284.6875	285	284.7	284.69
789.875	790	789.9	789.88
7.974375	8	8.0	7.97
0.92875	1	0.9	0.93
0.995	1	1.0	1.00

B1 Non-recurring
$1 \div 2 = 0.5$
$1 \div 4 = 0.25$
$1 \div 5 = 0.2$
$1 \div 8 = 0.125$
$1 \div 10 = 0.1$

Recurring
$1 \div 3 = 0.3333...$
$1 \div 6 = 0.16666...$
$1 \div 7 = 0.142857142857...$
$1 \div 9 = 0.111111...$
$1 \div 11 = 0.0909090...$
$1 \div 12 = 0.08333333...$

B2
$0.3333333 \longrightarrow 0.3$
$0.1666666 \longrightarrow 0.2$
$0.142857142857 \longrightarrow 0.1$
$0.1111111 \longrightarrow 0.1$
$0.090909 \longrightarrow 0.1$
$0.0833333 \longrightarrow 0.1$

p 18

A1
(a) $^-8$ (b) 5   (c) $^-20$
(d) $^-6$ (e) $^-41$ (f) 22
(g) $^-11$ (h) 25   (i) 21
(j) 12   (k) $^-76$ (l) $^-18$

A2
(a) 29   (b) $^-15$ (c) 37
(d) 13   (e) $^-70$ (f) 83   (g) 14
(h) 21   (i) $^-38$ (j) $^-53$ (k) $^-21$

B
(a) 4   (b) $^-8$ (c) 16
(d) $^-7$ (e) 9   (f) 3
(g) 14   (h) 27   (i) $^-12$

p 19

Now try this!
HI : 50   AT: 70   OF: 52   MA: 18

p 20

A1
(a) 10 8 6 4 2 0 $^-2$ $^-4$ $^-6$ $^-8$ $^-10$
(b) $^-10$ $^-8$ $^-6$ $^-4$ $^-2$ 0 2 4 6 8 10

A2
(a) $^-12$ (b) $^-16$ (c) $^-18$
(d) $^-16$ (e) 12   (f) 14
(g) $^-30$ (h) $^-28$ (i) 100

B

×	$^-3$	$^-2$	$^-1$	0	1	2	3
3	$^-9$	$^-6$	$^-3$	0	3	6	9
2	$^-6$	$^-4$	$^-2$	0	2	4	6
1	$^-3$	$^-2$	$^-1$	0	1	2	3
0	0	0	0	0	0	0	0
$^-1$	3	2	1	0	$^-1$	$^-2$	$^-3$
$^-2$	6	4	2	0	$^-2$	$^-4$	$^-6$
$^-3$	9	6	3	0	$^-3$	$^-6$	$^-9$

p 21

C1
(a) $^-18$ (b) 18   (c) $^-18$
(d) $^-2$ (e) 2   (f) $^-2$

p 22

A
(a) 2, 5, 3, 6, 9, 10   (b) 5, 7
(c) 2, 4, 8, 41

B
(a) 2, 4, 8   (b) 3, 5, 491
(c) 2, 3, 5, 6, 9, 10, 11, 101   (d) 2, 13, 1847
(e) 2, 3, 4, 5, 6, 8, 9, 10, 199   (f) 2, 3, 4, 6, 8, 9, 457

p 23

C1
(a) 12, 15   (b) 15
(c) 12   (d) –
(e) 15, 18   (f) 18
(g) 12, 15, 18   (h) 12, 18

C2
(a) no   (b) yes
(c) yes   (d) no
(e) yes   (f) yes

Now try this!
11   13   17   22   23

p 24

A
(a) $2 \times 2 \times 2 \times 3$ (b) $2 \times 2 \times 3 \times 5$
(c) $2 \times 2 \times 2 \times 11$ (d) $2 \times 2 \times 3 \times 3$
(e) $2 \times 5 \times 5$ (f) $2 \times 2 \times 3 \times 7$

B
(a) 2×3^2 (b) $3^2 \times 5$
(c) $2^2 \times 5^2$ (d) $2^2 \times 3^3$
(e) $2^2 \times 5 \times 7$ (f) 2×3^4

p 25

C1
(a) $2^3 \times 3^2$ (b) 2×3^3
(c) $2^3 \times 3 \times 5$ (d) $2^2 \times 3 \times 13$
(e) $2^4 \times 3 \times 5$ (f) $2 \times 3^2 \times 5^2$
(g) 2×7^3 (h) $2 \times 3 \times 7^2$
(i) $2^2 \times 3^4$ (j) $2 \times 3^3 \times 7$

C2
(a) HCF $= 2^2 \times 3 = 12$
(b) HCF $= 2 \times 3 \times 5 = 30$
(c) HCF $= 2 \times 7^2 = 98$
(d) HCF $= 2 \times 3^3 = 54$

C3
(a) LCM $= 2^3 \times 3 \times 5 \times 13 = 1560$
(b) LCM $= 2^4 \times 3^2 \times 5^2 = 3600$
(c) LCM $= 2 \times 3 \times 7^3 = 2058$
(d) LCM $= 2^2 \times 3^4 \times 7 = 2268$

Now try this!
(a) 2, 4, 8, 16, 32, 64
(b) 3, 9, 81
(c) 5, 25

p 26

A2
(a) 4   (b) 5   (c) 7
(d) 8   (e) 11   (f) 12
(g) 2   (h) 4   (i) 3
(j) 6   (k) 7   (l) 8

B1
(a) 49   (b) 49   (c) 225
(d) 225   (e) 784   (f) 784

B2 Square numbers are always positive.

B3 8 and $^-8$

p 27

C1
(a) 8.6   (b) 7.4
(c) 6.8   (d) 3.99

C2 approx 3.46

Now try this!
(a) 2.6
(b) 5.2
(c) 2.92

p 28

A2
(a) correct   (b) 2025   (c) correct
(d) 262 144   (e) correct   (f) correct
(g) correct   (h) 0.01   (i) correct

B
(a) $17^2 = 289$
(b) $31^2 = 961$ **or** $30^2 = 900$
(c) $49^2 = 2401$ **or** $59^2 = 3481$
(d) $77^2 = 5929$
(e) $8^3 = 512$ **or** $6^3 = 216$
(f) $21^3 = 9261$
(g) $15^3 = 3375$
(h) $33^3 = 35\,937$ **or** $25^3 = 15\,625$ **or** $44^3 = 85\,184$
(i) $(25 + 44)^3 = 328\,509$

p 30

A1 Approximations:
(a) $\frac{1}{8}$ (b) $\frac{1}{4}$ (c) $\frac{3}{8}$ (d) $\frac{1}{2}$
(e) $\frac{5}{8}$ (f) $\frac{3}{4}$ (g) $\frac{7}{8}$

A2
(a) $\frac{3}{4}$ (b) $\frac{1}{3}$ (c) $\frac{1}{12}$ (d) $3\frac{1}{4}$
(e) $1\frac{1}{2}$ (f) $1\frac{3}{4}$ (g) $2\frac{1}{12}$ (h) $\frac{5}{6}$
(i) $4\frac{5}{6}$ (j) $2\frac{5}{12}$ (k) $2\frac{7}{12}$ (l) $5\frac{1}{60}$

B (b) $\frac{1}{36}$

p 31
C1 B D F
C2 C F
C3 (a) C F
(b) They are square numbers.
(c) 49, 64, 81, 100
(d) Yes, 81 (every third number is a multiple of 9).

Now try this!
All the fractions can be shown except for $\frac{7}{9}$.

p 32
A (a) $\frac{3}{5}$ (b) $\frac{15}{26}$ (c) $\frac{8}{21}$ (d) $\frac{2}{5}$
(e) $\frac{8}{13}$ (f) $\frac{2}{3}$ (g) $\frac{1}{3}$ (h) $\frac{8}{15}$
(i) $\frac{20}{29}$ (j) $\frac{2}{3}$ (k) $\frac{3}{4}$ (l) $\frac{28}{33}$
B1 (a) $\frac{2}{9}$ (b) $\frac{1}{4}$ (c) $\frac{1}{3}$ (d) $\frac{1}{9}$
(e) $\frac{1}{12}$
B2 (a) $\frac{1}{6}$ (b) $\frac{7}{48}$ (c) $\frac{5}{12}$ (d) $\frac{1}{12}$
(e) $\frac{3}{16}$

p 33
C1 (a) $\frac{1}{15}$ (b) $\frac{1}{6}$ (c) $\frac{22}{45}$ (d) $\frac{7}{18}$
(e) $\frac{32}{45}$
C2 (a) $\frac{3}{10}$ (b) $\frac{11}{15}$ (c) $\frac{4}{5}$
C3 (a) $\frac{3}{5}$ $\frac{2}{5}$ (b) $\frac{7}{15}$ $\frac{8}{15}$ (c) $\frac{4}{7}$ $\frac{3}{7}$

p 34
A1 (a) $\frac{7}{25}$ (b) $\frac{8}{25}$ (c) $\frac{12}{25}$ (d) $\frac{16}{25}$
(e) $\frac{18}{25}$ (f) $\frac{21}{25}$ (g) $\frac{24}{25}$ (h) $\frac{1}{8}$
(i) $\frac{11}{40}$ (j) $\frac{3}{8}$ (k) $\frac{56}{125}$ (l) $\frac{5}{8}$
(m) $\frac{7}{8}$ (n) $\frac{116}{125}$
A2 (a) $\frac{1}{8}$ $\frac{3}{8}$ $\frac{5}{8}$ $\frac{7}{8}$ (b) They all end in 25 or 75.
B $0.375 \longrightarrow \frac{3}{8}$ $\frac{9}{24}$ $\frac{27}{72}$
$0.125 \longrightarrow \frac{1}{8}$ $\frac{12}{96}$
$0.475 \longrightarrow \frac{19}{40}$ $\frac{76}{160}$ $\frac{38}{80}$
$0.625 \longrightarrow \frac{5}{8}$ $\frac{20}{32}$ $\frac{60}{96}$
$0.64 \longrightarrow \frac{32}{50}$ $\frac{16}{25}$ $\frac{192}{300}$
$0.875 \longrightarrow \frac{7}{8}$ $\frac{56}{64}$

p 35
C (a) 0.25 (b) 0.2
(c) 0.4 (d) 0.125
(e) 0.6 (f) 0.375
(g) 0.625 (h) 0.8
(i) 0.75 (j) 0.875

Now try this!
They are all recurring decimals.

p 36
A1

÷	2	3	4	5	6	7	8	9
1	$\frac{1}{2}$	$\frac{1}{3}$	$\frac{1}{4}$	$\frac{1}{5}$	$\frac{1}{6}$	$\frac{1}{7}$	$\frac{1}{8}$	$\frac{1}{9}$
2	1	$\frac{2}{3}$	$\frac{1}{2}$	$\frac{2}{5}$	$\frac{1}{3}$	$\frac{2}{7}$	$\frac{1}{4}$	$\frac{2}{9}$
3	$1\frac{1}{2}$	1	$\frac{3}{4}$	$\frac{3}{5}$	$\frac{1}{2}$	$\frac{3}{7}$	$\frac{3}{8}$	$\frac{1}{3}$
4	2	$1\frac{1}{3}$	1	$\frac{4}{5}$	$\frac{2}{3}$	$\frac{4}{7}$	$\frac{1}{2}$	$\frac{4}{9}$
5	$2\frac{1}{2}$	$1\frac{2}{3}$	$1\frac{1}{4}$	1	$\frac{5}{6}$	$\frac{5}{7}$	$\frac{5}{8}$	$\frac{5}{9}$
6	3	2	$1\frac{1}{2}$	$1\frac{1}{5}$	1	$\frac{6}{7}$	$\frac{3}{4}$	$\frac{2}{3}$
7	$3\frac{1}{2}$	$2\frac{1}{3}$	$1\frac{3}{4}$	$1\frac{2}{5}$	$1\frac{1}{6}$	1	$\frac{7}{8}$	$\frac{7}{9}$
8	4	$2\frac{2}{3}$	2	$1\frac{3}{5}$	$1\frac{1}{3}$	$1\frac{1}{7}$	1	$\frac{8}{9}$
9	$4\frac{1}{2}$	3	$2\frac{1}{4}$	$1\frac{4}{5}$	$1\frac{1}{2}$	$1\frac{2}{7}$	$1\frac{1}{8}$	1

A2 The numbers increase in equal amounts as you move down the columns, e.g. the dividing by 2 column increases in increments of one-half, the dividing by 3 column increases in increments of one-third, and so on. Also when a number in the rows is a multiple of the dividend, then the answer is a whole number.
B1 (a) $1\frac{3}{4}$ (b) $1\frac{2}{7}$ (c) $2\frac{2}{3}$
(d) $1\frac{4}{5}$ (e) $1\frac{1}{3}$ (f) $3\frac{1}{2}$
(g) $2\frac{1}{3}$ (h) $2\frac{1}{4}$ (i) $1\frac{3}{5}$
B2 (a) 1.75 (b) 1.2857142 (c) 2.66666
(d) 1.8 (e) 1.33333 (f) 3.5
(g) 2.333333 (h) 2.25 (i) 1.6

p 37
C1

÷	2	3	4	5	6	7	8	9
1	0.5	0.3̇	0.25	0.2	0.16̇	0.1̇42857̇	0.125	0.1̇
2	1	0.6̇	0.5	0.4	0.3̇	0.2̇85714̇	0.25	0.2̇
3	1.5	1	0.75	0.6	0.5	0.4̇28571̇	0.375	0.3̇
4	2	1.3̇	1	0.8	0.6̇	0.5̇71428̇	0.5	0.4̇
5	2.5	1.6̇	1.25	1	0.83̇	0.7̇14285̇	0.625	0.5̇
6	3	2	1.5	1.2	1	0.8̇57142̇	0.75	0.6̇
7	3.5	2.3̇	1.75	1.4	1.16̇	1	0.875	0.7̇
8	4	2.6̇	2	1.6	1.3̇	1.1̇42857̇	1	0.8̇
9	4.5	3	2.25	1.8	1.5	1.2̇85714̇	1.125	1

C2 (a) $\frac{1}{3}$ (b) $\frac{3}{8}$ (c) $\frac{5}{8}$ (d) $\frac{1}{6}$
(e) $3\frac{1}{2}$ (f) $1\frac{4}{5}$ (g) $2\frac{2}{3}$ (h) $\frac{8}{9}$
(i) $\frac{5}{6}$ (j) $\frac{1}{7}$ (k) $1\frac{1}{3}$ (l) $\frac{7}{8}$

Now try this!
(a) $1\frac{8}{11}$ (b) $7\frac{3}{11}$ (c) $\frac{8}{110}$
(d) $\frac{4}{11}$ (e) $1\frac{4}{11}$ (f) $\frac{2}{11}$

p 38
A (a) $\frac{3}{20}$ $\frac{1}{4}$ $\frac{3}{10}$ $\frac{3}{8}$ $\frac{2}{5}$ (b) $\frac{7}{12}$ $\frac{5}{8}$ $\frac{2}{3}$ $\frac{3}{4}$ $\frac{5}{6}$
(c) $\frac{4}{9}$ $\frac{5}{9}$ $\frac{11}{18}$ $\frac{3}{4}$ $\frac{5}{6}$ (d) $\frac{13}{24}$ $\frac{9}{16}$ $\frac{7}{12}$ $\frac{5}{8}$ $\frac{5}{6}$
(e) $\frac{7}{9}$ $\frac{31}{36}$ $\frac{7}{8}$ $\frac{11}{12}$ $\frac{17}{18}$ (f) $\frac{3}{10}$ $\frac{1}{3}$ $\frac{2}{5}$ $\frac{7}{15}$ $\frac{13}{25}$
B (a) $\frac{17}{35}$ $\frac{1}{2}$ $\frac{37}{70}$ $\frac{4}{7}$ $\frac{3}{5}$ (b) $\frac{11}{21}$ $\frac{23}{42}$ $\frac{4}{7}$ $\frac{2}{3}$ $\frac{5}{6}$
(c) $\frac{5}{7}$ $\frac{42}{56}$ $\frac{11}{14}$ $\frac{7}{8}$ $\frac{25}{28}$ (d) $\frac{1}{6}$ $\frac{2}{9}$ $\frac{13}{54}$ $\frac{7}{27}$ $\frac{5}{18}$

p 39
C1 (a) $\frac{3}{5}$ $\frac{5}{7}$ $\frac{7}{10}$ $\frac{3}{4}$ $\frac{17}{20}$ (b) $\frac{12}{15}$ $\frac{8}{15}$ $\frac{3}{5}$ $\frac{2}{3}$ $\frac{7}{10}$
(c) $\frac{4}{9}$ $\frac{5}{8}$ $\frac{2}{3}$ $\frac{7}{10}$ $\frac{3}{4}$ (d) $\frac{1}{6}$ $\frac{1}{4}$ $\frac{1}{3}$ $\frac{3}{8}$ $\frac{5}{12}$
C2 (a) History
(b) $\frac{18}{25}$ $\frac{76}{100}$ (or $\frac{19}{25}$) $\frac{29}{38}$ $\frac{36}{47}$ $\frac{4}{5}$

p 40
A1 (a) 24 (b) 77 (c) 40
(d) 36 (e) 15 (f) 100
(g) 24 (h) 84 (i) 56
A2 (a) $\frac{16}{24}$ (b) $\frac{18}{24}$ (c) $\frac{21}{24}$
(d) $\frac{49}{56}$ (e) $\frac{24}{27}$ (f) $\frac{28}{35}$
A3 (a) $2\frac{13}{56}$ (b) $2\frac{14}{45}$ (c) $1\frac{29}{36}$ (d) $1\frac{55}{84}$
B (a) $\frac{3}{40}$ (b) $\frac{13}{30}$ (c) $\frac{7}{24}$
(d) $\frac{11}{24}$ (e) $\frac{9}{35}$ (f) $\frac{13}{45}$

p 41
C1 Discuss errors in questions. These are the correct answers:
(a) $\frac{1}{8}$ (b) $\frac{1}{24}$ (c) $\frac{23}{42}$ (d) $\frac{1}{36}$

Now try this!
Answers might include:
(a) $\frac{1}{8} + \frac{1}{5}$ (b) $\frac{1}{3} + \frac{1}{12}$ (c) $\frac{1}{3} + \frac{1}{2}$ (d) $\frac{1}{9} + \frac{1}{6}$

p 42

A1 (a) 30   (b) 30   (c) 60
     (d) 48   (e) 65   (f) 49
     (g) 100   (h) 140   (i) 318

A2 (a) $3\frac{3}{4}$ (b) $2\frac{1}{4}$ (c) $3\frac{3}{8}$
     (d) $8\frac{1}{4}$ (e) $9\frac{3}{8}$

A3 (a) $6\frac{1}{4}$ inches   (b) $3\frac{3}{4}$ inches   (c) $5\frac{5}{8}$ inches
     (d) $13\frac{3}{4}$ inches (e) $15\frac{5}{8}$ inches

B (a) $3\frac{3}{4}$ (b) $5\frac{1}{3}$ (c) $2\frac{4}{5}$ (d) $2\frac{1}{4}$
   (e) $10\frac{1}{2}$ (f) $7\frac{1}{2}$ (g) $8\frac{1}{4}$
   (h) $5\frac{5}{7}$ (i) $3\frac{3}{5}$ (j) $6\frac{1}{9}$ (k) $2\frac{1}{10}$

p 43

C1 (a) $12\frac{1}{2}$ (b) $17\frac{1}{2}$ (c) 12   (d) $7\frac{1}{2}$
   (e) $10\frac{1}{2}$ (f) 10   (g) $8\frac{2}{5}$ (h) $22\frac{1}{4}$

C2 (a) 200 g   (b) $61\frac{1}{2}$ g   (c) 77 g   (d) $37\frac{1}{2}$ g

Now try this! True

p 44

A1 (a) 32   (b) 64   (c) 128   (d) 256

A2 (a) 48   (b) 96   (c) 32
     (d) 192   (e) 64   (f) 144

A3 (a) 60   (b) 150   (c) 50
     (d) 180   (e) 36   (f) 75

B1 (a) $16 \div \frac{1}{2} = 32$ (b) $16 \div \frac{1}{4} = 64$
   (c) $16 \div \frac{1}{8} = 128$ (d) $16 \div \frac{1}{16} = 256$

B2 (a) $24 \div \frac{1}{2} = 48$ (b) $24 \div \frac{1}{4} = 96$
   (c) $24 \div \frac{3}{4} = 32$ (d) $24 \div \frac{1}{8} = 192$
   (e) $24 \div \frac{3}{8} = 64$ (f) $24 \div \frac{1}{6} = 144$

B3 (a) $30 \div \frac{1}{2} = 60$ (b) $30 \div \frac{1}{5} = 150$
   (c) $30 \div \frac{3}{5} = 50$ (d) $30 \div \frac{1}{6} = 180$
   (e) $30 \div \frac{5}{6} = 36$ (f) $30 \div \frac{2}{5} = 75$

The answer is larger than the original number.

p 45

C (a) 30   (b) 15
   (c) 135   (d) 45
   (e) 72   (f) 24
   (g) 60   (h) 12
   (i) 270   (j) 30

Now try this! False

p 46

A (a) 180   168   12   2.4
   (b) 4.2   0.14   3.5   2.1

B (a) £1.92   (b) £4.08   (c) £9.66

p 47

C1 (a) 30%   (b) 84%
   (c) 65%   (d) 72%
   (e) 80%   (f) 55%

C2 (a) 1000   (b) 168
   (c) £2070   (d) £71.40

p 48

A (a) 19.6   (b) 3.78   (c) 13.02
   (d) 33.92   (e) 51.06   (f) 11.68
   (g) 79.21   (h) 88.36   (i) 98.01

B (a) £30.78   (b) £13.68   (c) £5.89
   (d) £31.62   (e) £63.08   (f) £47.61
   (g) £6.65   (h) £21.07   (i) £95.55

p 49

C1 6 out of 30 $\rightarrow$ 20%
   15 out of 40 $\rightarrow$ 37.5%
   9 out of 72 $\rightarrow$ 12.5%
   15 out of 240 $\rightarrow$ 6.25%
   12 out of 150 $\rightarrow$ 8%
   14 out of 56 $\rightarrow$ 25%
   18 out of 150 $\rightarrow$ 12%

C2 (a) 9   (b) 2.25   (c) £402.50
   (d) 80   (e) 6 612 000

Now try this!
64%

p 50

A1 (a) 15%   (b) 13%   (c) 39%

A2 (a) Morning Chorus
   (b) Dawn Mix
   (c) Soft-bill Mix

A3 (a) Morning Chorus
   (b) Soft-bill Mix

A4 (a) Soft-bill Mix
   (b) Soft-bill Mix

B1 (a) $\frac{1}{10}$ 0.1   10%
   (b) $\frac{3}{4}$ 0.75   75%
   (c) $\frac{27}{100}$ 0.27   27%

B2 (a) $\frac{1}{100}$ 0.01   1%
   (b) $\frac{2}{5}$ 0.4   40%
   (c) $\frac{81}{100}$ 0.81   81%

B3 (a) $\frac{8}{25}$ 0.32   32%
   (b) $\frac{2}{25}$ 0.08   8%
   (c) $\frac{3}{8}$ 0.375   37.5%

p 51

C1 (a) 1.96 g   (b) 510.86 g   (c) 168.3 g   (d) 56 250 g
   (e) 63 750 g

C2 (a) 694 200 g   (b) 39 000 g   (c) 39 000 g   (d) 7800 g

Now try this!
(a) 28.2316 g   (b) 2.46 g   (c) 8.7777 g
(d) 0.882 g   (e) 0.1764 g   (f) 4.1275 g

p 52

A1 £7.56   £13.34   £106.08   £162.40
   £311.32   £43.52   £669.53   £217.80
   £130.66   £2362.50   £2745.60   £1259.70
   £28 449   £6138   £1138.10   £2000.20

A2 (a) £174   (b) £558
   (c) £2437.50

B £6.75   £51.75   115%
   £23.80   £108.80   128%
   £87.04   £223.04   164%
   £119.60   £379.60   146%
   £326.54   £1452.54   129%

p 53

C (a) 320   (b) £44 720
   (c) 46.4 mph   (d) 3360 g
   (e) £318   (f) 97 552
   (g) 53 428   (h) £1129.05
   (i) £173 750   (j) £41.81

Now try this!
£36 160

p 54

A1 (a) £66
   (b) £342
   (c) £62.50
   (d) £547.20

A2 £6.75   £38.25   85%
   £23.80   £61.20   72%
   £87.04   £48.96   36%
   £119.60   £140.40   54%
   £109.46   £732.54   87%
   £326.54   £799.46   71%

B (a) £1457.50   (b) 34 mph
   (c) 234   (d) 47.52 kg

p 55
Now try this!
(a) It will double.
(b) It will nearly halve.
(c) It will nearly double.
(d) There will be none left.

p 56
A   (a) 5 : 6 : 7   (b) 2 : 3 : 5
      (c) 2 : 4 : 3   (d) 6 : 3 : 1
      (e) 5 : 15 : 18   (f) 2 : 4 : 1
      (g) 4 : 3 : 6   (h) 3 : 1 : 2
      (i) 5 : 7 : 8   (j) 31 : 34 : 25
      (k) 7 : 40 : 20   (l) 8 : 11 : 10

B   (a) $\frac{5}{18}$ $\frac{1}{3}$ $\frac{7}{18}$ (b) $\frac{1}{5}$ $\frac{3}{10}$ $\frac{1}{2}$
      (c) $\frac{2}{9}$ $\frac{4}{9}$ $\frac{1}{3}$ (d) $\frac{3}{5}$ $\frac{3}{10}$ $\frac{1}{10}$
      (e) $\frac{5}{38}$ $\frac{15}{38}$ $\frac{9}{19}$ (f) $\frac{2}{7}$ $\frac{4}{7}$ $\frac{1}{7}$
      (g) $\frac{4}{13}$ $\frac{3}{13}$ $\frac{6}{13}$ (h) $\frac{1}{2}$ $\frac{1}{6}$ $\frac{1}{3}$
      (i) $\frac{1}{4}$ $\frac{7}{20}$ $\frac{2}{5}$

p 57
C   (a) £16   £24   £28
      (b) 72˚   108˚   180˚
      (c) 228 g flour   152 g sugar   304 g butter
      (d) £36   £42
      (e) 30˚   45˚
      (f) 66 g flour   44 g sugar

Now try this!
1   (a) 800 m
      (b) 4400 m
      (c) 9600 m

2   (a) $\frac{1}{2}$ cm
      (b) 10 cm
      (c) 16 cm

p 58
A   £2.75   £3.05   £4.98
      £5.50   £6.10   £9.96
      £8.25   £9.15   £14.94
      £11   £12.20   £19.92
      £13.75   £15.25   £24.90
      £16.50   £18.30   £29.88

B2 Approximately
      (a) 6.4 km
      (b) 14.4 km
      (c) 1.9 miles

p 59
C   (a) US $55.48   (b) 4217.74 yen
      (c) HK $545.28   (d) €75.84
      (e) 235.68 pesos   (f) 241.56 Egypt pounds
      (g) 9981 kronur   (h) 9121.28 rupees

Now try this!
(a) £15.50
(b) £21.10
(c) £14.20
(d) £35.70
(e) £76.17
(f) £30.10
(g) £6.43
(h) £812